Third Edition

BIOLOGY 101

Laboratory Manual

Owens Community College

Robert Connour II, Tara Carter, Anne Bullerjahn,
Joanne Roehrs, April Andrews, Matthew Gosses

VAN-GRINER

Biology 101

Laboratory Manual
Third Edition
Owens Community College

Robert Connour II, Tara Carter, Anne Bullerjahn, Joanne Roehrs, April Andrews, Matthew Gosses

Printed in the United States of America
10 9 8 7 6 5 4
ISBN: 978-1-61740-443-6

Van-Griner Publishing
Cincinnati, Ohio
www.van-griner.com

CEO: Mike Griner
President: Dreis Van Landuyt
Project Manager: Maria Walterbusch
Customer Care Lead: Julie Reichert

Bullerjahn 443-6 Sp18
183543-320018
Copyright © 2019

TABLE OF CONTENTS

iv

LABORATORY 1
THE SCIENTIFIC METHOD
AND METRIC SYSTEM

PART 1 THE SCIENTIFIC METHOD

LEARNING OBJECTIVES

- Identify the steps of the scientific method.

- Learn how the scientific method is used to answer questions and solve problems.

- Practice using the scientific method in a simple experiment.

INTRODUCTION

The scientific method is a series of steps that scientists use to investigate natural processes and answer questions about how those processes function. Used properly, the scientific method adds to our knowledge of the world around us. There are several steps to the scientific method, each of which are defined below:

1. **Observation**—This is the first step, and it occurs whenever you see something happen that causes you to ask a question.

2. **Question**—Once you have made a detailed observation, you next come up with a question. For example: Why did that insect fly in that direction? Why did the corn grow better in this field than in the other field?

3. **Hypothesis**—A hypothesis is formed after much more observation and is a tentative explanation for the observed phenomena. A good hypothesis will lead to a prediction.

4. **Experiments**—These are carried out to deliver results that will either support or go against the hypothesis.

5. **Conclusion**—After many experiments and observations, a conclusion is drawn that either supports or refutes the original hypothesis.

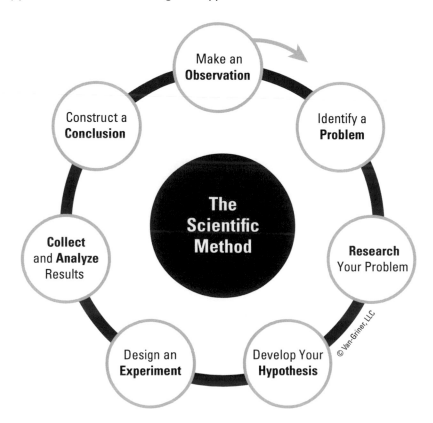

Figure 1.1 Scientific Method.

LAB ACTIVITY

When apples are sliced the inside is immediately exposed to air and will start to oxidize. The enzyme polyphenol oxidase reacts with the oxygen in the air and the iron in the apple causing the fruit to oxidize and turn brown. One way to prevent this is to lower the pH of the surface of the apple, which will prevent the enzyme from functioning. Another way is to seal the surface off from air.

In this lab exercise we will test different substances to see which is the best at preventing oxidation, and thus browning, of the apple slices.

PROCEDURES

1. Obtain an apple and an apple slicer or knife and cut the apple into wedges.

2. Prepare three cups as follows:

   a. One with 250 mL of tap water;

   b. One with 250 mL of tap water and 40 mL of vinegar;

   c. One with 250 mL of tap water and 40 mL of lemon juice.

3. Place one slice of apple in each cup and leave a slice out exposed to the air as a control.

4. Observe what is happening to the apple slices every 15 minutes for one hour and fill in Table 1.5 on page 15.

5. Answer questions about the scientific method on page 16.

PART 2 METRIC SYSTEM

LEARNING OBJECTIVES

- Identify basic metric units of length, volume, mass, and temperature.

- Measure length, volume, mass, and temperature in metric units.

- Calculate density and volume.

- Apply conversions between metric units.

- Recall the appropriate prefix to use when using the metric system.

- Be able to identify basic equipment found in the laboratory.

The **metric system** (sometimes referred to as the International System of Units or SI) is the standardized system of measurements used throughout the world and in the scientific community. In the United States, units of measurements are of the English system and include pounds, inches, feet, degrees Fahrenheit, etc. In the United States, of course, there are exceptions where the metric system is often used such as in 2-liter bottles of soda and in races such as a 5 k (kilometers).

The basic units of the metric system include the meter (m) for measuring length, liter (L) for measuring volume (usually liquid volume), kilogram (kg) for measuring mass and degrees Celsius (°C) for measuring temperature.

The metric system is based on units of ten and is often called a decimal based system. This allows for easier conversions between units. Units of ten in the metric system are indicated by prefixes before the base units (i.e., kilometer, millimeter, etc.).

Table 1.1 Conversions from English to Metric.

English Unit of Measurement	=	Metric Unit of Measurement
1 inch	=	2.5 centimeters
1 foot	=	30 centimeters
1 yard	=	0.9 meter
1 mile	=	1.6 kilometers
1 ounce	=	28 grams
1 pound	=	0.45 kilogram
1 fluid ounce	=	30 milliliters
1 pint	=	0.47 liter
1 quart	=	0.95 liter
1 gallon	=	3.8 liters
1 cup	=	0.24 liter

The basic metric units commonly used in biology laboratory include the following:

- Meter (m)—the basic unit of length

- Liter (L)—the basic unit of volume (for liquid)

- Kilogram (kg)—the basic unit of mass

- Degrees Celsius (°C)—the basic unit of temperature

Table 1.2 Prefixes Used in the Metric System.

Multiplication Factor	Prefix	Symbol
$1,000,000,000 = 10^9$	giga	G
$1,000,000 = 10^6$	mega	M
$1,000 = 10^3$	kilo	k
$100 = 10^2$	hecto	h
$10 = 10^1$	deka	da
$0.1 = 10^{-1}$	deci	d
$0.01 = 10^{-2}$	centi	c
$0.001 = 10^{-3}$	milli	m
$0.000\ 001 = 10^{-6}$	micro	µ
$0.000\ 000\ 001 = 10^{-9}$	nano	n

CONVERSION BETWEEN METRIC UNITS

Since the metric system is measured in units of 10 (example: 1 km = 1,000 m) it is easy to convert between units. The decimal place has to be moved from the right or left depending on if you are converting to a smaller or larger unit. If you are converting to a larger unit of measurement (example: kilometers from meters) the decimal place is moved to the left. If converting to a smaller unit of measurement (example: centimeters from meters), the decimal point is moved towards the right.

Table 1.3 Metric Conversions.

K_{ing}	H_{enry}	D_{ied}	$U_{nusually}$	$D_{rinking}$	$C_{hocolate}$	M_{ilk}
Kilo	**Hecto**	**Deca**	**Unit**	**Deci**	**Centi**	**Milli**
$10 \times 10 \times 10 \times$ LARGER than a unit	$10 \times 10 \times$ LARGER than a unit	$10 \times$ LARGER than a unit	**Meter** *(length)* **Liter** *(liquid volume)* **Gram** *(mass/weight)*	$10 \times$ SMALLER than a unit	$10 \times 10 \times$ SMALLER than a unit	$10 \times 10 \times 10 \times$ SMALLER than a unit
1 kilo = 1,000 units	1 hecto = 100 units	1 deca = 10 units	1 unit	10 deci = 1 units	100 centi = 1 units	1,000 milli = 1 units
km = kilometer kL = kiloliter kg = kilogram	hm = hectometer hL = hectoliter hg = hectogram	dam = decameter daL = decaliter dag = decagram	m = meter L = liter g = gram	dm = decimeter dL = deciliter dg = decigram	cm = centimeter cL = centiliter cg = centigram	mm = millimeter mL = milliliter mg = milligram
Example 5 kilo	Example 50 hecto	Example 500 deca	Example 5,000 units	Example 50,000 deci	Example 500,000 centi	Example 5,000,000 milli

Divide numbers by **10** if you are getting bigger (same as moving decimal point one space to the left).

Multiply numbers by **10** if you are getting smaller (same as moving decimal point one space to the right).

EXAMPLES OF CONVERSION

To convert kilograms to grams multiply kilograms by 1,000 or 10^3.

- 5 kg = 5,000 grams

To convert liters to milliliters divide liters by 0.001 or 10^{-3}.

- 3 L = 3,000 mL

FUN FACT

If in England the metric system is used, then why does the U.S. still use the English system of measurement?

The United States have used certain metric units for years such as liters for fluid (mainly soda) and kilometers for racing distances. However, in this country, the old English system is used much more than in other countries around the world, even in England. The discrepancy dates back to the American colonists who came from Britain. The colonists brought England's current way of measurement (then the English system) with them. France was the first country to develop the metric form of measurement. Political tensions between France and the new America kept the U.S. from adopting the metric system that was beginning to become universal. It wasn't until after the Civil War and after most of Europe had adopted the decimal based metric system that President Johnson gave the go ahead to use the metric system as a form of measurement. However, the adoption of the metric system has been very slow in the States despite amendments passed in Congress designating the metric system as the preferred system of measurement. However, as time goes by, the metric system is being used more and more in American society.

© Jean-Loup Charmet/Science Source

Figure 1.2 Metric System. An illustration showing the institution of the metric system in France, 1800. This standardized system of weights and measures was introduced into France under the supervision of the chemist Jean Chaptal, whom Napoleon had placed in charge of education. The system was recognized (but not adopted) by the UK and other countries during the nineteenth century. In 1960, a scientific conference on weights and measures recommended implementation of an international metric system including the meter, the kilogram, and the second as standard units. SI (Système International) units are now accepted as standard in many areas of usage.

LAB ACTIVITIES

Measurements for Metric System Lab Activities can be written in Table 1.6 on page 17.

LENGTH AND AREA

1. Examine a meter stick or a metric ruler. Look at the intervals for millimeter, centimeter, decimeter, and meter.

2. Measure the following:

    a. Length of a page

    b. Diameter of a penny

    c. Thickness of a book

    d. Height of yourself or lab partner

    e. Height of a beaker

3. What is the area of your lab manual?

    Area is calculated by multiplying the length of an item by its width:

    A = length (L) × width (W)

MASS

Mass is the quantity of matter of an object and the amount of gravitational force exerted onto that object. A gram is equal to the mass of one cubic centimeter (cm^3) of water at 4°C, which is the temperature of water at its densest, or heaviest per unit area.

There are a few ways to measure the mass or weight of an object and they include the triple beam balance that uses three horizontal beams with weights that counter balance the object you are weighing or the top load balance which has a digital display. When using either balance, make sure that the measuring pan is clean. Also, if you are using a weigh dish to hold your sample, make sure the balance is tared, or zeroed, or you must remember to subtract the mass of the weigh dish from your sample.

1. Measure the mass of the following:

    a. Penny or other coin

    b. Empty beaker

    c. Beaker containing 50 mL of water

    d. Paper clip

    e. Marble or pebble

    f. Pencil or pen

VOLUME

Volume is the amount of space that is occupied by an object and can be measured in two ways. If trying to measure a liquid sample, liters are used. Graduated cylinders or beakers are the common lab equipment used to do this. If measuring a non-liquid item such as the volume of a classroom, the length × width × height is used and the unit is cubed, such as m^3.

1. Measure the volume of the following:

    a. Volume of this classroom

    b. Volume of 50 grams of water

    c. Volume of the inside of a coffee cup

    d. Volume of a marble or pebble

    e. Volume of a pencil

DENSITY

Density is calculated by the mass per unit volume. In this lab, the unit used to describe density will be in g/ml (or gram per milliliter).

D = mass/volume

Some items such as a stopper may take up the same amount of space or area but have different densities or masses per unit volume. Rubber stoppers are generally denser than stoppers made of cork.

1. What is the density of the following items:

   a. A pebble

   b. 50 mL of water at room temperature

   c. Density of a pencil

2. How did you determine the density of the pencil?

TEMPERATURE

Temperature is defined as the amount of heat, or kinetic energy, in a system. The metric scale of temperature is measured in degrees Celsius.

Table 1.4 Common Temperatures in °C.

Temperature	Reaction
0°C	Water freezes
4°C	Water at its densest This is how the weight of 1 gram is calculated. (1 cc, or cubic centimeter, or cm^3 of H_2O at its densest at 4°C is equal to 1 gram.)
25°C	Room temperature
37°C	Body temperature
100°C	Water boils

1. Measure the following:

    a. Temperature of the lab room

    b. Temperature of outside air

    c. Temperature in a refrigerator

    d. Temperature of hot water

    e. Temperature of cold or ice water

CONVERSIONS

1. Convert the following:

    a. 500 meters to kilometers

    b. 50 liters to milliliters

    c. 25 centimeters to meters

    d. 600 millimeters to meters

    e. 742 milliliters to liters

USING APPROPRIATE MEASUREMENTS

It is important to recognize that certain types of metric measurements are more appropriate to use than others. For example, you would not want to weigh a rhinoceros in grams. The number would be too large to use, since grams are a fairly small unit of measurement. Kilograms would make more sense to use when weighing a large animal. If you were weighing a small animal such as a mouse, grams would be a perfectly acceptable unit of measure.

1. What unit would you use to measure the following?

    a. Weigh a cricket

    b. Determine the height of a skyscraper

    c. Measure the distance from your seat to the door

    d. Measure the distance from here to San Diego

IDENTIFY BASIC LABORATORY EQUIPMENT

1. Identify the basic lab equipment you have used in this lab and that is found around the lab. This equipment will be used during each lab session.

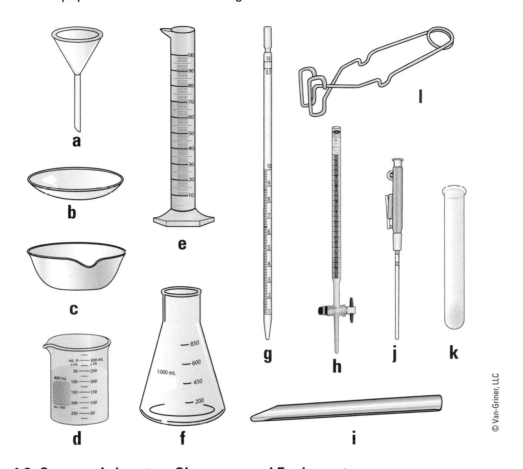

Figure 1.3 Common Laboratory Glassware and Equipment.

a. _____

b. _____

c. _____

d. _____

e. _____

f. _____

g. _____

h. _____

i. _____

j. _____

k. _____

l. _____

© Van-Griner, LLC

NOTES

Biology 101 Laboratory Manual

LABORATORY 1 REVIEW
THE SCIENTIFIC METHOD
AND METRIC SYSTEM

PART 1 THE SCIENTIFIC METHOD

DATA

TABLE 1.5 Scientific Method with Apples.

	15 Minutes	30 Minutes	45 Minutes	1 Hour
Control				
H_2O				
H_2O and Vinegar				
H_2O and Lemon Juice				

QUESTIONS

1. What are the parts of the scientific method?

   _____

   _____

   _____

2. What would your hypothesis be for the experiment you just performed?

   _____

   _____

   _____

3. Why is it important that experiments be conducted and data be collected?

   _____

   _____

   _____

4. Based on your results, what can you conclude about keeping apples from turning brown?

   _____

   _____

5. Are there any other factors that could have affected your results?

   _____

   _____

6. If you were going to move forward with this experiment what other types of substances might you test?

   _____

   _____

7. Turn in data table for scientific method on page 15 or as directed by your instructor.

NAME:_____   DATE:_____

PART 2 METRIC SYSTEM

DATA

TABLE 1.6 Measurement Results.

Activity	Items to Measure	Metric Measurement
Length and Area	Length of a page	
	Diameter of a penny	
	Thickness of a book	
	Height of yourself or lab partner	
	Height of a beaker	
	Area of lab manual	
Mass	Penny or other coin	
	Empty beaker	
	Beaker containing 50 mL of water	
	Paper clip	
	Marble or pebble	
	Pencil or pen	
Volume	Volume of classroom	
	Volume of 50 grams of H_2O	
	Volume of the inside of a coffee cup	
	Volume of a marble or pebble	
	Volume of a pencil	

Activity	Items to Measure	Metric Measurement
Density	A pebble	
	50 mL of water at room temperature	
	Density of a pencil	
Temperature	Temperature of lab room	
	Temperature of outside air	
	Temperature in a refrigerator	
	Temperature of hot water	
	Temperature of cold or ice water	
Conversions	500 meters to kilometers	
	50 liters to milliliters	
	25 centimeters to meters	
	600 millimeters to meters	
	742 milliliters to liters	
Appropriate Measurements	Weight of a cricket	
	Height of skyscraper	
	Distance from your seat to the door	
	Distance from here to San Diego	

NAME: _____   DATE:_____

QUESTIONS

1. What are some advantages of using the metric system as a standard use of measurement?

    _____

    _____

2. What are some disadvantages of using the metric system as a use of measurement?

    _____

    _____

3. Why is it important for the global community of scientists to use the same units of measurement?

    _____

    _____

4. Why is the metric system easier to use than the English system?

    _____

    _____

5. How did you measure the density of a pencil?

    _____

    _____

6. How did you measure the volume inside a coffee cup?

    _____

    _____

7. Why is it important to use the appropriate measurement? For example, why would you measure your pet hippopotamus in kilograms instead of milligrams?

    _____

    _____

8. Turn in data for measurement on pages 17 and 18, or as directed by your instructor.

NOTES

LABORATORY 2
MICROSCOPY

LEARNING OBJECTIVES

- Describe basic care and use of the **compound** and **dissecting scopes.**

- Distinguish basic parts and functions of the compound and dissecting scopes.

- Calculate the total **magnification** and **diameter, radius,** and **area of the field of view** for each objective lens.

- Examine organisms using the compound and dissecting scopes.

- Prepare a wet mount.

- Compare and contrast the compound and dissecting scopes.

INTRODUCTION

The microscope is a tool that has been proven invaluable to the scientist. The compound light microscope allows us to see things too small for the unassisted eye. Microscopy opens up other worlds to us that exist beyond the capabilities of human vision.

Care must be taken to carry the microscope in the proper fashion. One hand is to be placed on the arm and the other under the base. The scope should be carried close to the body. The "suitcase" method should not be employed!

A critical chore that must be completed before and after each use of the microscope is cleaning the **ocular** and **objective lenses.** Lens paper and cleaning solution are the only items to be used on the lenses. A piece of lens paper is folded in fours and then 1–2 drops of cleaning solution are applied. All lenses are cleaned with a blotting motion. If too much solution is applied, it will leave water marks on the lens. The use of Kimwipes on any lenses is grounds for dismissal from lab.

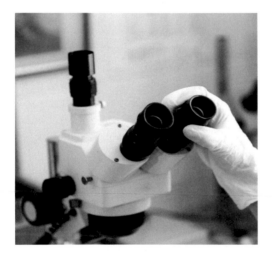 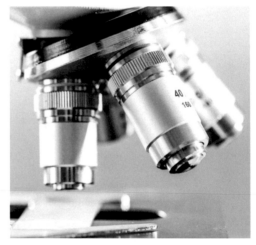

Figure 2.1 How to Clean Microscope Lenses. Before and after use, always clean all lenses. Oculars are pictured on the left and the objective lenses are shown on the right.

When observing a specimen on a microscope slide, always begin with the physically smallest objective on the **revolving nosepiece.** Be sure that it is properly clicked into place. This is the 4× or scanning objective. The number indicating the magnification of the objective is located on the side of the objective lens. You may use both the **coarse and fine adjustment knobs** for focusing the **specimen** when using the **4× objective lens.**

If greater magnification is desired, rotate the **10× (low power) objective** into place. You may use both the coarse and fine adjustment knobs for focusing the specimen. Never use the coarse adjustment when the **40× (high power) objective** is used. Damage may occur to the microscope slide or microscope.

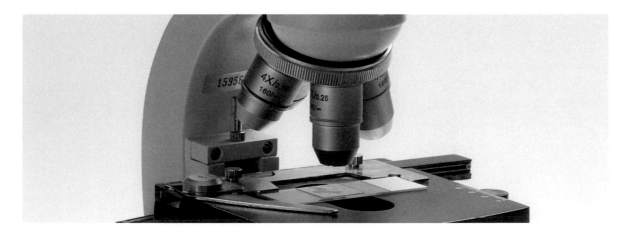

Figure 2.2 Locating Objectives and Focus Knobs. Each objective is labeled with its magnification. The larger ring is the coarse focus knob and the smaller ring is the fine focus knob.

After you have concluded your microscope activities for the day, clean the lenses, click into place the 4× objective, raise the **stage,** wrap the cord around the base of the scope, and replace the **dust cover.**

Figure 2.3 The Dust Cover. Proper storage will assure that your microscope remains in working order.

The parts of the compound light microscope include the **oculars, body tube, arm, stage, stage clips, base, light, objective lenses, condenser, iris diaphragm, and coarse and fine adjustment knobs.** The ocular lens is what you look through and its magnification is 10×. There may be two oculars, referred to as binocular, or one ocular, referred to as monocular. The body tube is the passage way for light entering the oculars. The arm facilitates carrying. The stage clips hold the microscope slide on the stage. The base provides for the physical foundation of the scope. The light is transmitted from below the specimen, then through the specimen into the objective lenses. The condenser focuses the light from the source to the specimen. The iris diaphragm regulates the light passing through the specimen. The adjustment knobs provide coarse and fine focusing of the specimen.

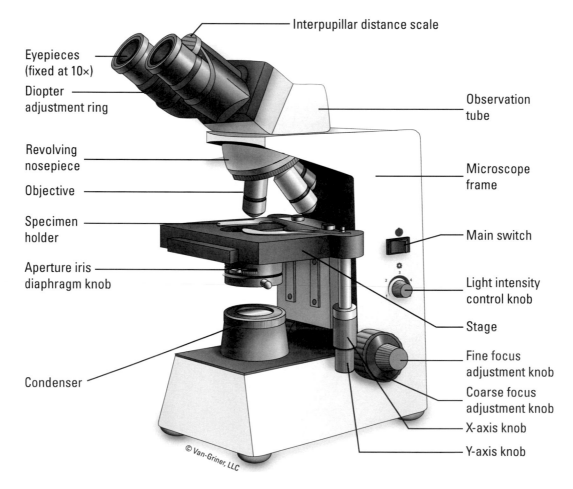

Figure 2.4 The Parts of the Compound Light Microscope. Learn the parts of the microscope and understand the functions of each part.

Magnification increases the apparent size of a specimen. It is the ratio of an object's image to its real size. The magnification of the ocular lens is always 10×. The magnification of the objective lenses is 4×, 10×, and 40×. To calculate **total magnification,** the magnification of the ocular lens is multiplied by the magnification of the objective lens in place. For example, if a specimen is being examined with the 4× objective lens, the total magnification is 40× (10 × 4 = 40).

Figure 2.5 Magnification. The apparent size of a specimen is increased with magnification. The image becomes larger than the actual size as magnification increases.

Resolution (resolving power) is the ability to distinguish two points as separate points, a specified distance apart. It is a measure of the clarity of the image or the ability to see fine detail. The resolving power of the unaided eye is 0.1 mm. This means that when we look at two points that are no closer than 0.1 mm, we see them as two separate points. If the two points are any closer, we only see one point.

Parfocal refers to a focused specimen remaining so when another objective lens is clicked into place. And parcentered means that a specimen remains centered in your field of view when the objective is switched to another.

The field of view (FOV) is the area that you see when you look through the ocular and objective lenses. It's a circle. It is important to know the size of your field of view to determine the size of the specimen you are examining. The diameter helps you know how long an object is and the area helps you know how much space it takes up.

Figure 2.6 Field of View (FOV). The area that you are able to see when looking through the ocular and objective lenses is known as the field of view (FOV). The field of view changes as magnification changes.

To measure the **diameter of the field of view (dFOV)** when using the 4× objective, place the **millimeter** side of a **metric ruler** across the middle of the opening in the stage. Focus on the markings and count the number of millimeters across the diameter of the circle (FOV).

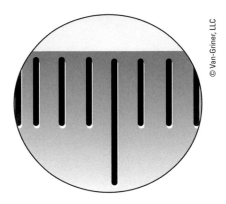

© Van-Griner, LLC

Figure 2.7 Measuring the Diameter of the Field of View of the 4× Objective. Place the ruler markings across the diameter of the circle and count the millimeters.

In order to determine the dFOV for the 10× and 40× objectives, an equation is used. For these objectives the magnification is too great and the ruler markings too far apart to get an accurate measurement with a ruler. The equations follow:

For the 10× objective: dFOV 4× × Mag 4× = dFOV 10× × Mag 10×

For the 40× objective: dFOV 4× × Mag 4× = dFOV 40× × Mag 40×

Plug in what you are given: dFOV 4×, Mag 4×, Mag 10×, Mag 40×, then solve for dFOV 10× and dFOV 40×, where

dFOV 4× = what you measured in millimeters with the ruler

Mag 4× = the magnification of the 4× objective

Mag 10× = the magnification of the 10× objective

Mag 40× = the magnification of the 40× objective

To calculate the **area of the field of view (aFOV),** use the formula for the area of a circle. The **radius** is half the diameter. Multiply 3.14 (pi) by the radius squared. You can do this for each field of view to get an idea of how large your specimen is at any given magnification.

The **depth of field** refers to the thickness of an object that is in sharp focus. Although microscopic specimens may appear two dimensional, they do have three dimensions. There is a thickness to them. When examining a wet mount of algae, for example, you may see some cells are clear while others are out of focus. The depth of field is greater under lower magnifications. This means that more of the specimen is focused. A thin depth of field occurs at higher magnifications. Less of the specimen is clearly focused.

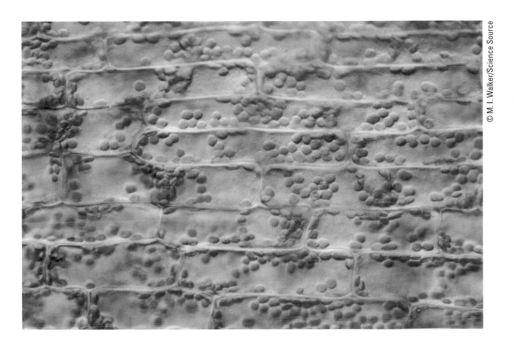

Figure 2.8 Depth of Field. Magnification 160×.

Contrast is the amount of difference between the lightest and darkest parts of the image. **Stain** makes specimens more visible by creating contrast between dark and light areas. Most microscopic specimens are clear or transparent without stain. If stain is used however, be aware that it will kill a living specimen. **Wet mounts** are used for examining fresh, living specimens.

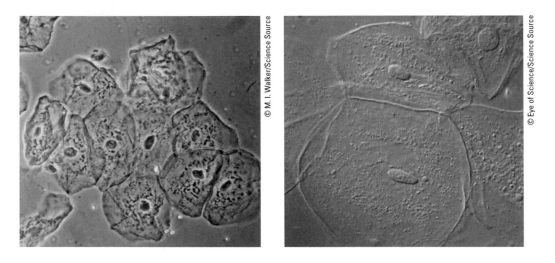

© M. I. Walker/Science Source

© Eye of Science/Science Source

Figure 2.9 Contrast. Stain provides a contrast between the darkest and lightest parts of a specimen. More detail may be observed when the epithelial cell on the left is stained with methylene blue. Magnification 50× at 35 mm for image on left. Magnification 530× for image on right.

To prepare a wet mount, a specimen is placed on a microscope slide or **concavity slide** within a drop of water. A cover slip is placed over the water drop at a 45-degree angle. It is slowly dropped into place. Carelessness with this last step may create bubbles under the cover slip and a field of view that is difficult to negotiate.

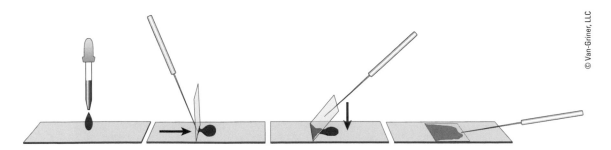

© Van-Griner, LLC

Figure 2.10 Mount Preparation. Mounts are used to view living specimens. Care should be taken that air bubbles are not trapped beneath the cover slip.

Some specimens are too large for viewing under a compound light microscope, but closer scrutiny is achieved by the use of a **dissecting or stereoscopic microscope.** Dissecting microscopes are always **binocular** and never **monocular.** This provides the observer with a three dimensional view of a specimen. The working distance of the dissecting scope is much larger than the compound scope. It is large enough to perform **dissection** on large specimens inside of a dissecting pan. Because of this, the FOV is larger than that of the compound microscope.

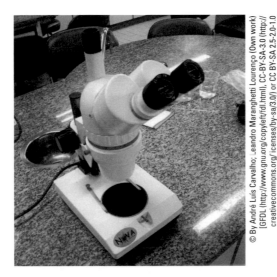

Figure 2.11 The Stereoscopic or Dissecting Microscope. Large specimens may be examined using a dissecting microscope. Specimens are observed in three dimensions.

Magnification and resolution are not as great with the dissecting scope as with the compound microscope. Magnification is rarely greater than 50×. DOF is greater for the dissecting scope. The lower the magnification of an image, the greater is the thickness of the specimen that is in focus. Since the dissecting scope has a lower magnification power than the compound scope, the depth of field is greater. The **light source** for the dissecting scope is **reflected light**. It comes from above the specimen. The light strikes the specimen and bounces back to the eye. This is in contrast to the **transmitted light** provided for by the compound scope.

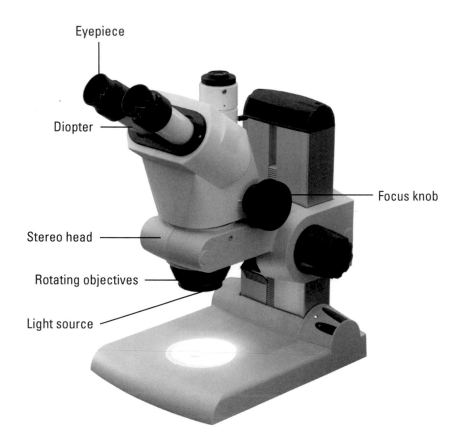

Eyepiece

Diopter

Focus knob

Stereo head

Rotating objectives

Light source

Figure 2.12 Parts of the Dissecting or Stereoscopic Microscope. Some dissecting scopes require the multiplication of the ocular lenses to obtain total magnification and others do not. Ask your instructor if you have any questions.

LAB ACTIVITIES

BASIC CARE AND USE OF THE COMPOUND MICROSCOPE

1. Obtain a microscope and practice carrying the microscope properly.

2. Remove the dust cover, unwind the cord, and plug it into an outlet.

3. Clean the oculars and objective lenses with lens paper and cleaning solution according to instructions.

PARTS AND FUNCTIONS OF THE COMPOUND MICROSCOPE

1. Identify the parts of the microscope and learn their functions.

2. Obtain a prepared slide of the newsprint letter "e."

3. Beginning with the 4× objective, locate the letter "e" and focus.

4. Manipulate the light intensity and iris diaphragm to get the clearest view.

5. Familiarize yourself with changes in light requirements as you work through each of the objectives.

6. **Never** use the coarse focus knob when the 40× objective is in place.

7. **Do not** use the 100× objective lens.

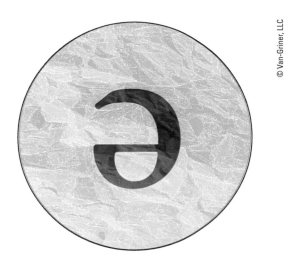

© Van-Griner, LLC

Figure 2.13 The Letter "e" under the Microscope. The images are inverted. Notice that the letter moves to the left when you move it to the right and vice versa.

CALCULATION OF TOTAL MAGNIFICATION

1. Calculate total magnification of the specimen when using the 4×, 10×, and 40× objectives and fill in the table.

2. Draw a sketch of the letter "e" at 40× total magnification and 400× total magnification and note the differences that you observe.

Table 2.1 Total Magnification. Total magnification of a specimen is calculated by multiplying the objective lens magnification by the ocular lens magnification.

Objective	Ocular	Total Magnification

CALCULATION OF THE DIAMETER OF THE FIELD OF VIEW (dFOV)

1. Physically measure the diameter of the FOV for the 4× objective using a metric ruler and fill in the table.

2. Using the equation dFOV 4× × Mag4× = dFOV 10× × Mag10×, calculate the dFOV for the 10× objective and fill in the table.

3. Using the equation dFOV 4× × Mag4× = dFOV 40× × Mag40×, calculate the dFOV for the 40× objective and fill in the table.

Table 2.2 Diameter of the FOV. The diameter of the FOV (dFOV) for the 4× objective is measured with a ruler or micrometer. The dFOV for the 10× and 40× objectives must be calculated using an equation because the magnification is too great to accurately observe the ruler measurements.

dFOV 4×	dFOV 10×	dFOV 40×

CALCULATION OF THE AREA OF THE FIELD OF VIEW (aFOV)

1. Calculate the radius for each FOV (rFOV). The radius is one half the diameter of the field of view.

Table 2.3 The Radius of the FOV. The radius is one half the diameter of the field of view.

rFOV 4×	rFOV 10×	rFOV 40×

2. Using the equation for the area of a circle, calculate the aFOV for each objective lens and fill in the table.

Table 2.4 The Area of the FOV. The area of the FOV is calculated using the formula for the area of a circle. The radius is half the diameter. Multiply 3.14 (pi) by the radius squared.

aFOV 4×	aFOV 10×	aFOV 40×

DETERMINATION OF DEPTH OF FIELD (DOF)

1. Obtain a prepared slide of three different colored threads.

2. Beginning with the 4× objective focus the threads.

3. Sketch a drawing of the threads at 40× total magnification.

4. As you work with the 10× and 40× objectives make observations about the clarity and focus of the three threads.

5. Sketch a drawing of the threads at 400× total magnification.

6. Determine which color thread is on the bottom, in the middle, and on top, and indicate this order on the two drawings.

PREPARATION OF A WET MOUNT

1. Obtain a microscope slide, cover slip, pipet, and living specimen.

2. Prepare a wet mount and examine living specimens using the compound microscope.

3. Determine the total magnification.

4. Sketch a drawing of one specimen and indicate total magnification.

USE OF THE DISSECTING MICROSCOPE

1. Obtain a dissecting microscope and clean the lenses.

2. Identify the parts of the dissecting microscope.

3. Choose two specimens and examine them.

4. Determine the total magnification.

5. Draw a sketch of each specimen and indicate total magnification.

COMPARING AND CONTRASTING THE COMPOUND AND DISSECTING MICROSCOPES

1. Determine the differences and similarities of the dissecting microscope with the compound microscope with respect to the following:

    a. Oculars

    b. Light source

    c. Magnification

    d. Resolution

    e. FOV and DOF

    f. Working distance

    g. Specimens

Table 2.5 Differences between the Compound and Dissecting Scopes. Record your comparisons of the two types of microscopes you will use this semester.

Feature	Compound	Dissecting
Oculars		
Light Source		
Magnification		
Resolution		
FOV		
DOF		
Working Distance		
Specimens		

NOTES

Biology 101 Laboratory Manual

LABORATORY 2 REVIEW
MICROSCOPY

QUESTIONS

1. What is total magnification? Explain what that means.

_____

_____

_____

_____

2. What is the resolving power of the unaided eye? Explain.

_____

_____

_____

_____

3. What critical action must always be taken before and after using a microscope?

_____

_____

_____

_____

4. What is the function of the oculars? Objectives? Condenser? Iris diaphragm? Stage? Coarse adjustment? Fine adjustment?

_____

_____

_____

_____

5. What does parfocal mean? Parcentered?

_____

_____

_____

_____

6. Why must specimens viewed with a compound microscope be thin?

_____

_____

_____

_____

7. Why are some specimens stained with dyes?

_____

_____

_____

_____

8. Recall our laboratory activities. When using the 40× high power objective lens, how many times was the letter "e" magnified? Explain your answer.

_____

_____

_____

_____

9. What are the advantages of knowing the diameter of the field of view at a given magnification?

_____

_____

_____

_____

10. If the diameter of the field of view when using the 4× objective is 4 mm, what is the area of the field of view when using the 4×, 10×, and 40× objectives? Show all work.

_____

_____

_____

_____

11. Which objective, 10× or 40×, provides the greatest depth of field? Explain.

_____

_____

_____

12. Of the three magnifications that you used in lab, which magnification requires the most illumination for best clarity and contrast? Explain.

_____

_____

_____

13. For what purposes are wet mounts used?

_____

_____

_____

14. Compare the dissecting scope and compound scope with respect to oculars, magnification, resolution, working distance, specimen, light source, size of FOV, and DOF.

_____

_____

_____

NAME: _____ DATE: _____

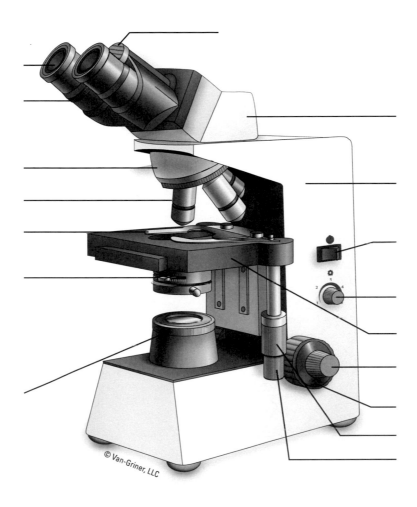

© Van-Griner, LLC

LABORATORY 3
THE CELL

LEARNING OBJECTIVES

- Identify differences and similarities of **prokaryotic** and **eukaryotic** cells.

- Name the structures of the cell and the functions of those structures.

- Characterize different types of cells.

- Distinguish animal cells from plant cells.

- Examine **bacteria, cyanobacteria, plant cells, animal cells,** and **protist cells** with the microscope.

INTRODUCTION

The **cell** is the basic, structural, functional unit of life. There is no unit smaller than a cell that carries on the activities of life. Structure and function of the cell are intrinsically bound. A cell's structure determines its function. If its structure were to change, its function would be altered also.

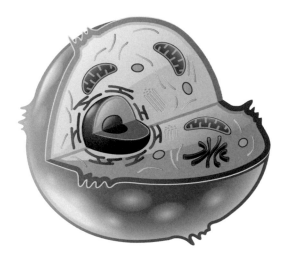

Figure 3.1 The Cell. The basic, structural, functional unit of life.

Taxonomists categorize living organisms into three **Domains.** They are **Archaea, Bacteria,** and **Eukarya.** The organisms that compose Archaea and Bacteria are prokaryotic. And the organisms that compose Eukarya are eukaryotic. This distinction is based on cell type. Prokaryotic cells have no membrane-bound nucleus nor do they have any membrane-bound organelles.

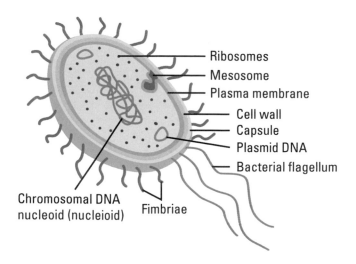

Figure 3.2 The Cell. The basic, structural, functional unit of life.

Conversely, eukaryotic cells do. A **nucleus** is a membrane-bound organelle that contains the bulk of the genetic material of a cell. It is responsible for guiding the cell's activities. **Organelles** ("little organs") are membrane-bound structures that have characteristic shapes and specific functions within the cell.

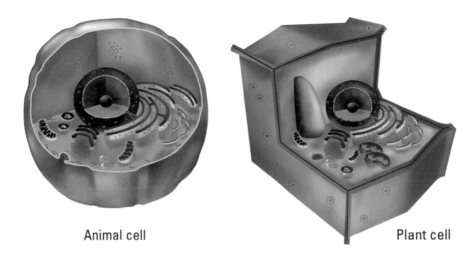

Animal cell   Plant cell

Figure 3.3 Eukaryotic Cells. Eukaryotic cells have both a nucleus and membrane-bound organelles.

Generally, prokaryotic cells have a cell wall, plasma membrane, cytoplasm, nucleoid, and ribosomes. Some, but not all, have a flagellum (singular) or flagella (plural). Additional structures that are sometimes found include pili and plasmids.

The bacterial cell wall composed of **peptidoglycan,** a carbohydrate and amino acid polymer, gives the bacterial cell its shape. It also functions in protection. The **plasma membrane** regulates the comings and goings of substances into and out of the cell. The **cytoplasm** contains a semi fluid (gelatinous) substance that suspends chemicals and structures. The **nucleoid** is made up of a single bacterial chromosome—a double helix in a circle. It is not surrounded by a membrane. **Ribosomes** are the sites of protein synthesis for the cell.

The **flagellum** functions in locomotion. There may be one, many, or none present in bacteria. Its structure and movement is very different from that of flagella found in eukaryotic cells. **Pili** (plural) are used in the transfer of genetic material from one bacterial cell to another. A pilus (singular) is a tube-like structure that some bacteria produce. It attaches to another similar bacterium to allow transfer to occur. This is not sexual reproduction, but it is as close as it gets in bacteria! Reproduction is achieved asexually by way of **binary fission.** Basically, the cell grows bigger and splits in two.

Figure 3.4 The Bacterial Cell. Many structures are found in the bacterial cell but no organelles.

Cyanobacteria are the largest of the prokaryotic cells. ***Oscillatoria*** and ***Gloeocapsa*** are two examples of cyanobacteria. They are commonly referred to as blue-green algae. However, they are not algae! They are prokaryotic! They contain the pigment, chlorophyll *a,* in thylakoids and appear green in color. They have no chloroplasts. A mucilaginous sheath surrounds the cells.

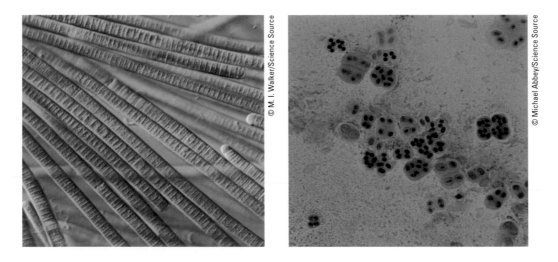

Figure 3.5 Two Examples of Cyanobacteria. Left is *Oscillatoria,* a filamentous cyanobacterium. Right is *Gloeocapsa,* a colonial form of cyanobacterium. Both are prokaryotic and enclosed in a mucilaginous sheath. Magnification unknown for image on left. Magnification 100× at 35 mm for image on right.

The bacterium, *Lactobacillus,* is a lot smaller than cyanobacteria. It contains no chlorophyll. It can change milk into yogurt by fermentation.

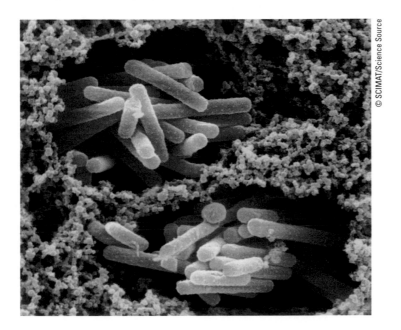

Figure 3.6 *Lactobacillus.* This bacterium does not photosynthesize, but converts milk into yogurt by fermentation. Magnification 7000×, image width 13.6 μm.

Bacterial cells, including cyanobacteria, are prokaryotic. But, everything else has eukaryotic cells—plants, fungi, protists, and animals. Eukaryotic cells have the characteristics that prokaryotic cells lack—a membrane-bound nucleus and membrane-bound organelles. Reproduction occurs both sexually and asexually through **meiosis** and **mitosis.**

The **endoplasmic reticulum** is a membrane-bound organelle that functions in cellular metabolism. The **Golgi complex** packages substances used inside the cell and those destined to be exported. **Lysosomes** recycle cellular refuse. **Mitochondria** convert intermediates of glucose into the energy currency of the cell—**ATP** (adenosine triphosphate).

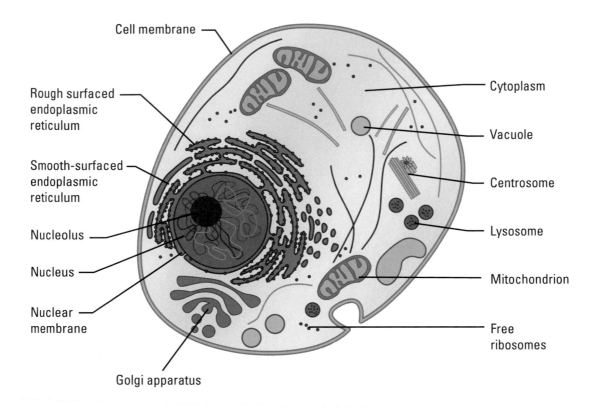

Figure 3.7 A Generic Animal Cell. An animal cell has many organelles, or "little organs" that have specific jobs.

Plant cells are bordered by cellulose cell walls. **Cellulose** is composed of **polysaccharides** (many simple sugars) and is the most abundant organic compound on Earth. Plant cells have plastids, small organelles such as chloroplasts and amyloplasts that contain pigments or nutrients. **Chloroplasts** are the organelles of photosynthesis and utilize the pigment chlorophyll *a,* which causes them to appear green. This site is where sugars are manufactured through the conversion of the light energy of the sun. **Amyloplasts** act as starch storage depots for the plant cell. They may be observed under the microscope in a thin slice of the potato. **Iodine,** a starch indicator, stains the amyloplasts a dark blue or purple color.

A **central vacuole** can compose 90% or more of the volume of a plant cell. It may store water or waste or some product of the plant cell such as latex (rubber plant). **Plasmodesmata** are used for plant cell to plant cell communication. Chemicals and fluids move back and forth between adjacent cells. **Cytoplasmic streaming** may sometimes be observed in living plant cells. It is the movement of the cytoplasm. This mixing assists in the movement of nutrients and chemicals to different parts of the cell.

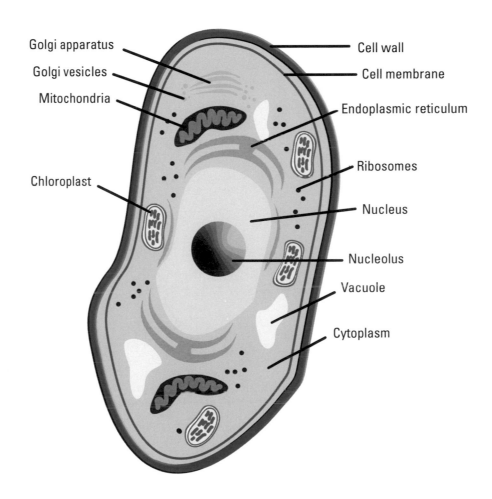

Figure 3.8 A Generic Plant Cell. Likewise, a plant cell has many organelles that provide the cell with a cohesive "team" that maintains smooth cellular operations.

Elodea is a common pond plant. **Chloroplasts** are easily observed within its cells with the compound microscope. They appear as oval or elliptical in shape. The **nucleus** is usually visible as a large, brownish oval. **Cytoplasmic streaming** may be observed as the heat from the microscope lamp increases kinetic energy.

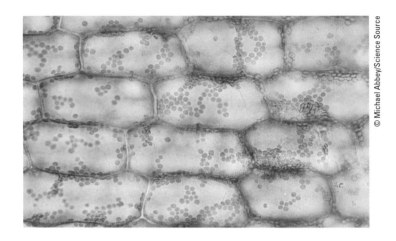

Figure 3.9 *Elodea*. The small green chloroplasts within the *Elodea* cells are the sites of photosynthesis. Magnification 100×.

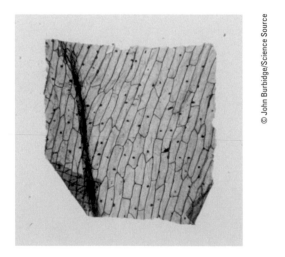

Figure 3.10 Onion Epithelia. Neutral red stain makes the onion cell nuclei "pop"! Magnification 18×.

Animal cells have many of the same structures as do plant cells, for instance, plasma membrane, cytoplasm, mitochondria, endoplasmic reticula, Golgi body, ribosomes, and nucleus. There are some structures present in animal cells that are absent in plant cells, such as **centrioles** for cell division. There are structures that animal cells do not have, that plant cells do. These include the cell wall, central vacuole, and chloroplasts.

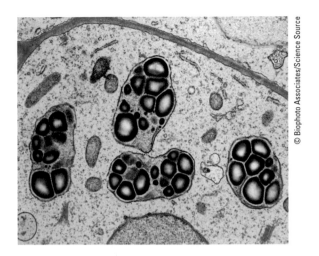

Figure 3.11 Amyloplasts. The potato cell stores starch in plastids called amyloplasts. Iodine provides their contrast with the surrounding potato cells. Magnification unknown.

An example of an animal cell often examined is the human epithelial cell. These are flat cells with an irregular edge. Typically, the **nucleus** and **nucleolus** is easily observed when stained with **methylene blue.**

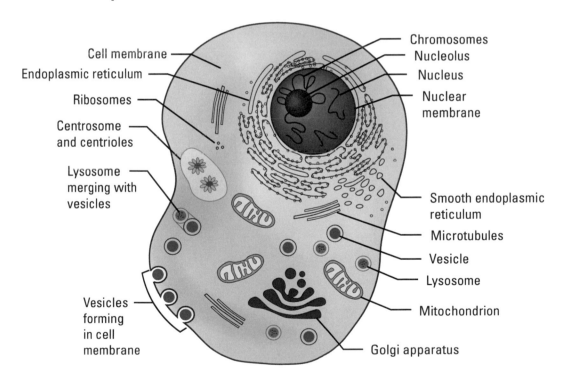

Figure 3.12 Organelles of the Animal Cell. Animal cells have centrioles for cell division activities.

Protists include algae, protozoa, and slime molds. Their diversity and complexity precludes placing them in one Kingdom according to some taxonomists! The **Amoeba** is a single-celled, irregularly-shaped protozoan that has many organelles. **Contractile vacuoles** are used to rid the cell of excess water and waste. **Phagocytic vacuoles** surround food particles, which are digested intracellularly. The mode of motility for Amoeba is called **amoeboid movement** and occurs by way of pseudopodia. **Pseudopods,** temporary extensions of the plasma membrane, extend and propel the amoeba in its locomotion.

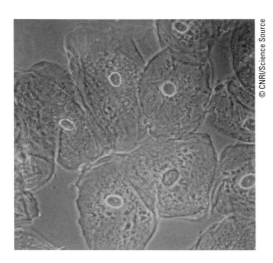
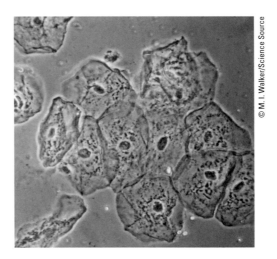

Figure 3.13 Human Epithelial Cells. The cheek cells on the left are better viewed when stained with methylene blue as on the right. Magnification unknown for image on left. Magnification 50× at 35 mm for image on right.

The single-celled protozoan, **Paramecium,** is rigid but flexible and has a faster, smoother motion as compared to the Amoeba. The mode of motility for the Paramecium is a surface covered by cilia. **Cilia** are short hair-like structures that constantly wave moving the cell through its aquatic environment. Contractile vacuoles are also used for removal of excess water and waste.

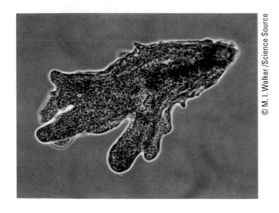
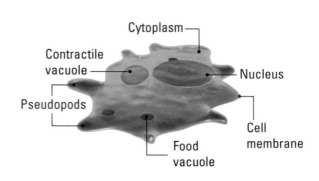

Cytoplasm

Contractile vacuole

Nucleus

Pseudopods

Cell membrane

Food vacuole

Figure 3.14 Amoeba. The Amoeba moves via pseudopods (false feet). Magnification 50× at 35 mm for image on left.

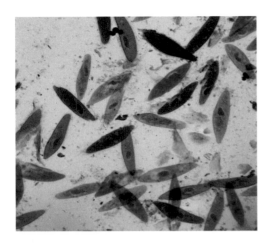 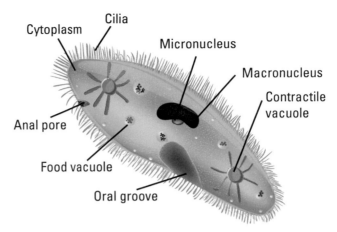

Figure 3.15 *Paramecium*. Cilia, short hair-like structures covering the pellicle, provide the cell with locomotion.

LAB ACTIVITIES

PROKARYOTIC CELLS—CYANOBACTERIA AND BACTERIA

1. Sketch a drawing of a generic bacterial cell and label the structures:

    a. Cell wall

    b. Plasma membrane

    c. Cytoplasm

    d. Nucleoid

    e. Ribosomes

    f. Plasmid

    g. Pili

    h. Flagellum

2. Review your notes on wet mount preparation.

3. Make wet mounts of two cyanobacteria, *Oscillatoria,* and *Gloeocapsa;* examine and sketch a drawing of each.

4. From yogurt, make a wet mount of the bacterium, *Lactobacillus;* examine and sketch a drawing.

EUKARYOTIC CELLS—PLANTS, ANIMALS, PROTISTS

PLANT CELLS

1. *Elodea*

    a. Make a wet mount with one leaf from *Elodea* placed right side up.

    b. Examine, observe cytoplasmic streaming, and sketch a drawing.

    c. Label cell wall, plasma membrane, cytoplasm, chloroplasts, nucleus, central vacuole.

2. Onion

    a. Make a wet mount of the tissue paper-like epidermis of the onion.

    b. Stain the mount for five minutes with neutral red, examine, and sketch a drawing; make a note whether or not chloroplasts are observed.

    c. Label cell wall, plasma membrane, cytoplasm, nucleus, nucleolus.

3. Potato

    a. Make a wet mount of a thin slice of potato.

    b. Stain the mount with iodine, examine, and sketch a drawing.

    c. Label amyloplast.

ANIMAL CELLS

1. Human Epithelial Cells

    a. Using the larger flat end of a toothpick, make a wet mount of the cheek cells from the inside of your mouth.

    b. Stain the mount with methylene blue, examine, and sketch a drawing.

    c. Label plasma membrane, cytoplasm, nucleus, nucleolus.

PROTIST CELLS

1. *Amoeba*

   a. Make a wet mount of *Amoeba;* if a living specimen is not available, examine a prepared slide of *Amoeba.*

   b. Examine and sketch a drawing.

   c. Label plasma membrane, cytoplasm, pseudopod, nucleus.

2. *Paramecium*

   a. Make a wet mount of *Paramecium;* if a living specimen is not available, examine a prepared slide of *Paramecium.*

   b. Examine and sketch a drawing.

   c. Label pellicle, cytoplasm, cilia.

UNKNOWN ORGANISM

1. Examine the unknown organism and sketch a drawing.

2. Answer the following questions about the observed unknown organism:

   a. Is it single-celled or multicellular?

   b. Is it prokaryotic or eukaryotic?

   c. Is it moving? How?

   d. Describe its shape.

   e. Are there any distinguishing features?

   f. Is it bacterial, plant, animal, or protist?

NOTES

Biology 101 Laboratory Manual

LABORATORY 3 REVIEW
THE CELL

QUESTIONS

1. **Tell me how** to properly write the scientific name of an organism. Give one example.

_____

_____

_____

_____

2. What is a cell?

_____

_____

_____

_____

3. How are eukaryotic cells **different** from prokaryotic cells? How are they **similar?**

_____

_____

_____

_____

4. What is the nucleoid region? What is its function? In which type of cell would you find one?

_____

_____

_____

_____

5. What two genera of cyanobacteria did you observe in lab? Did you see a **nucleus** in either one? If you did, describe it. If you did not, why not?

_____

_____

_____

_____

6. What makes up yogurt? What is the name of the bacterium that converts milk to yogurt?

_____

_____

_____

_____

NAME: _____   DATE:_____

7. What is the nucleus of a cell? What is its function?

_____

_____

_____

_____

8. What is the mitochondrion of a cell? What is its function?

_____

_____

_____

9. What is a chloroplast? What is its function? In what cell did you see chloroplasts?

_____

_____

_____

10. What is cytoplasmic streaming? In what cell might you observe it?

_____

_____

_____

11. What is the purpose of using a biological stain when microscopically examining cellular components?

_____

_____

_____

12. What is an amyloplast? What is its function? In which wet mount preparation did you observe amyloplasts?

_____

_____

_____

_____

13. How are animal cells **different** from plant cells? How are they **similar?**

_____

_____

_____

_____

14. Recall your observations of your own epithelial cells. Why did you stain the cells? What stain did you use?

_____

_____

_____

_____

15. Describe the mode of motility for both the *Amoeba* **and** *Paramecium.*

_____

_____

_____

_____

LABORATORY 4
FERMENTATION AND
PHOTOSYNTHESIS

LEARNING OBJECTIVES

- Recall the purpose of fermentation.

- Measure the amount of CO_2 produced by yeast grown on various carbon sources.

- Recall the stages of photosynthesis.

- Measure CO_2 uptake by *Elodea*.

- Separate pigments from spinach leaves.

- Determine R_f values for the pigments from spinach leaves, and draw conclusions about the chemical natures of the pigments.

- Recall how metabolism works and its importance.

- Recall the differences between aerobic respiration and fermentation.

- Recall and appreciate why photosynthesis is composed of the most important series of chemical reactions that occur on earth.

- Compare and contrast aerobic respiration with photosynthesis.

INTRODUCTION

Metabolism is the sum of all chemical reactions in a cell. Some of these reactions are **catabolic:** They break large molecules, like sugars, into smaller molecules, like carbon dioxide (CO_2) and water (H_2O). Catabolic reactions release energy. Other metabolic reactions are **anabolic:** They join small molecules together to make a large molecule. One example of this is protein synthesis in which amino acids are linked together to make a protein. Anabolic reactions require energy. All reactions in a cell are catalyzed by **enzymes.** That means that enzymes control whether or not a reaction occurs and how fast it goes. In this laboratory, you will study fermentation, a catabolic reaction, and photosynthesis, an anabolic reaction. Both are types of metabolism.

Fermentation is a way that cells can make ATP without oxygen, or **anaerobically.** In fermentation, a sugar molecule is broken a little bit. When chemical bonds are broken, energy is released. Cells can capture some of this energy and use it to make ATP (adenosine triphosphate), the energy molecule of the cell. In fermentation in yeast, a glucose molecule ($C_6H_{12}O_6$) is broken into two ethanol molecules (C_2H_5OH), and two molecules of CO_2 and two molecules of ATP are made:

$$C_6H_{12}O_6 \longrightarrow 2C_2H_5OH + 2CO_2 + 2ATP.$$

The amount of CO_2 produced is a way to measure the amount of fermentation occurring. The amount of CO_2 produced when the yeast are given different sugars is a way to measure the effectiveness of different sugars as energy sources. Glucose and fructose are monosaccharides or simple sugars. Sucrose is a disaccharide made of glucose and fructose linked together. In order to use fructose or sucrose, the yeast must first rearrange fructose and sucrose into glucose.

In **photosynthesis,** organisms such as plants are able to capture **light** energy and make ATP, which is then used to link together CO_2 and H_2O to make carbohydrates such as glucose.

$$6CO_2 + 6H_2O \xrightarrow{\text{light}} C_6H_{12}O_6 + 6O_2$$

In plants, these reactions occur in **chloroplasts.** Within chloroplasts, there are disk-shaped structures called **thylakoids.** The pigment molecules that capture light energy are in the thylakoid membranes. There is also a cytoplasm-like component within chloroplasts called **stroma.** This is where the carbon-fixation reactions called the Calvin cycle occur. During the Calvin cycle, molecules of CO_2 are incorporated into other sugar molecules so that the final product is glucose.

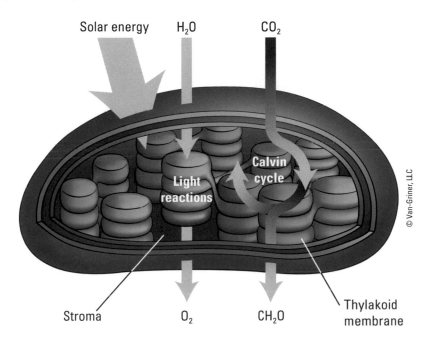

Figure 4.1 Overview of Photosynthesis. Photosynthesis includes the light reactions when energy is collected and O_2 is released, and the Calvin cycle reactions when carbohydrate (CH_2O) is formed.

In this part of the lab, you will separate the different photosynthetic pigments from spinach. You will also observe the uptake of CO_2 by the aquatic plant *Elodea* by measuring the pH change using phenol red.

LAB ACTIVITIES

FERMENTATION

For this procedure, you may use either fermentation tubes or small test tubes inside large test tubes.

1. Mark four small test tubes at the ⅔-full level.

2. Fill the test tubes to the ⅔-full line as follows:

    a. Tube 1: glucose solution

    b. Tube 2: fructose solution

    c. Tube 3: sucrose solution

    d. Tube 4: distilled water

3. Either fill the rest of the small test tube with the yeast solution **or** add the sugars or water to four fermentation tubes and fill them the rest of the way with the yeast solution. There should be no bubbles in the fermentation tubes.

4. If using the small test tubes, slide large test tubes over the small test tubes, hold the small test tube in place with your finger, and invert the tubes so that the small test tube is upside-down. Place the tubes in a test tube rack.

    If using the fermentation tubes, put a small piece of Parafilm® over the opening and poke a hole in the Parafilm.

© Van-Griner, LLC

Figure 4.2 Fermentation Tube.

5. Place the tubes in the 37°C incubator. After 20 minutes, check the tubes to see if there is a measurable bubble in the top. If the bubble is too small, leave the tubes in the incubator at least 10 more minutes.

6. Remove the tubes from the incubator and measure the size of the gas bubble in millimeters. Record the results in Table 4.1.

Table 4.1 Fermentation.

Tube	Contents	Beginning Gas Height (mm)	Ending Gas Height (mm)	Net Change (mm)
1				
2				
3				
4				

CO₂ UPTAKE

1. Fill a large test tube ⅓ full with phenol red. Add an equal amount of distilled water so that the test tube is ⅔ full. You may use a beaker for this step—it might be less messy.

2. Use a straw to blow **gently** into the phenol red solution until it just turns yellow.

3. Add a fairly large piece of *Elodea* to the test tube, making sure that it is completely covered by the phenol red solution.

4. Place the test tube in a test tube rack so that the *Elodea* is exposed to the stationary light.

5. Create another test tube with phenol red turned yellow, but do not add any plant to this tube. This is your control.

6. Check the color of the solutions every 10 minutes for 30–40 minutes and record changes.

Table 4.2 *Elodea* in Phenol Red.

Time	Color
10 Minutes	
20 Minutes	
30 Minutes	
40 Minutes	

CHROMATOGRAPHY OF PHOTOSYNTHETIC PIGMENTS

Green plants are green because they **absorb** the red and blue wavelengths in white light and **reflect** the green wavelengths. Pigment molecules absorb light energy. In green plants, the pigment molecules are in the thylakoid membranes. The pigments in green plants are chlorophyll *a,* chlorophyll *b,* carotenes, and xanthophylls.

Chromatography is a technique for separating pigment molecules from each other based on chemical properties, such as size of the molecules and how soluble they are in a particular **solvent.** Smaller, more soluble molecules stay in solution longer and travel farther on the chromatography paper. Larger, less soluble molecules do not travel as far. The solvent you use in this procedure contains acetone and petroleum ether, so you should work with it under a fume hood.

1. Construct the chromatography apparatus: Obtain a large test tube and a stopper with a hook. Be careful when handling chromatography paper so that you only handle the edges. Trim the chromatography paper so that it has a point at the bottom and it hangs from the hook without touching the sides or the bottom of the tube.

2. Find a fresh, young, green spinach leaf and roll it so that there are several layers. Use the edge of a coin to transfer a line of green pigment onto the chromatography paper about 1–2 cm from the pointed end. Use a pencil (not a pen) to mark the location of the line.

3. Place the small amount of chromatography solvent in the bottom of the large test tube. Put the stopper in the tube so that the pointed tip of the chromatography paper hanging from the hook is barely in the solvent.

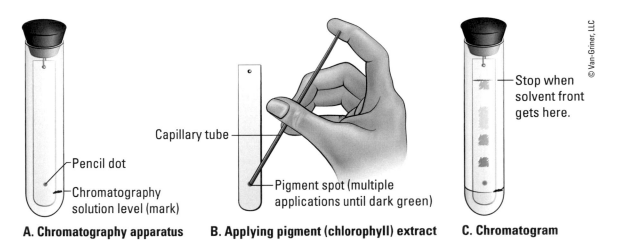

A. Chromatography apparatus   B. Applying pigment (chlorophyll) extract   C. Chromatogram

Figure 4.3 Chromatography of Photosynthetic Pigments.

4. Monitor the progress of the solvent as it is absorbed by the chromatography paper. When the solvent edge is about ½ cm from the hook, disassemble the apparatus and use a pencil to mark the highest place the solvent was absorbed.

5. There should be four colored bands on the chromatography paper. Carotenes are orange-yellow and at or near the top. Xanthophylls are yellow and should be below the carotenes. Chlorophyll *a* is blue-green and should be close to the bottom, and chlorophyll *b* is more olive green and should be the lowest band. Measure the distance each pigment traveled in mm from the starting line at the bottom.

6. Calculate R_f (ratio-factor) values for each pigment. Divide the distance each pigment traveled by the distance the solvent traveled.

R_f = distance traveled by the solute (pigment)/distance traveled by the solvent

TABLE 4.3 R_f Values of Photosynthetic Pigments.

Pigment	Distance Moved (mm)	R_f Values
Carotenes		
Xanthophylls		
Chlorophyll *a*		
Chlorophyll *b*		
Solvent		1

NOTES

Biology 101 Laboratory Manual

LABORATORY 4 REVIEW FERMENTATION AND PHOTOSYNTHESIS

QUESTIONS

1. Define catabolism, anabolism, and metabolism.

_____

_____

_____

_____

2. What is fermentation? What is the overall reaction of fermentation?

_____

_____

_____

_____

3. In the fermentation experiment, the amount of fermentation that occurred was determined by measuring the gas bubble produced. What was the gas in the bubble?

_____

_____

_____

_____

4. Which sugar produced the most fermentation as measured by the size of the bubble?

_____

_____

_____

_____

5. Why was the sugar identified in Question 4 the most effective?

_____

_____

_____

_____

6. Did the fermentation tube with distilled water and no sugar produce a bubble? Why or why not?

_____

_____

_____

_____

NAME: _____ DATE: _____

7. What is aerobic respiration? How does it differ from fermentation?

_____

_____

_____

_____

8. What is photosynthesis? What is the overall reaction of photosynthesis?

_____

_____

_____

_____

9. Why did the color of the phenol red solution change when you blew into it through a straw?

_____

_____

_____

_____

10. Why did the color of the phenol red solution with the *Elodea* change when exposed to light?

_____

_____

_____

_____

11. Why do plants use more than one pigment?

_____

_____

_____

12. Which pigment had the largest R_f? Which pigment had the smallest R_f?

_____

_____

_____

13. What is the R_f? How is the R_f calculated?

_____

_____

_____

14. What does a small R_f indicate about the chemistry of the pigment?

_____

_____

_____

_____

15. Where in the plant cell are pigment molecules located?

_____

_____

_____

_____

LABORATORY 5
MITOSIS: CELL REPRODUCTION, AND
MEIOSIS: SEXUAL REPRODUCTION

LEARNING OBJECTIVES

- Know and understand the stages of the eukaryotic cell cycle.

- Identify the four stages of mitosis and understand what is occurring in each.

- Identify the stages of mitosis in both animal and plant cells and know how the process differs in each.

- Know and understand the stages of meiosis and why it is important for sexual reproduction.

- Understand the difference between haploid ($1n$) cells and diploid ($2n$) cells.

- Understand why meiosis is called "reduction division" and how the chromosomes are copied once and separated twice.

- Understand how crossing over and independent assortment lead to genetic variation.

- Understand how mitosis and meiosis relate to the human life cycle.

- Compare and contrast mitosis and meiosis.

INTRODUCTION

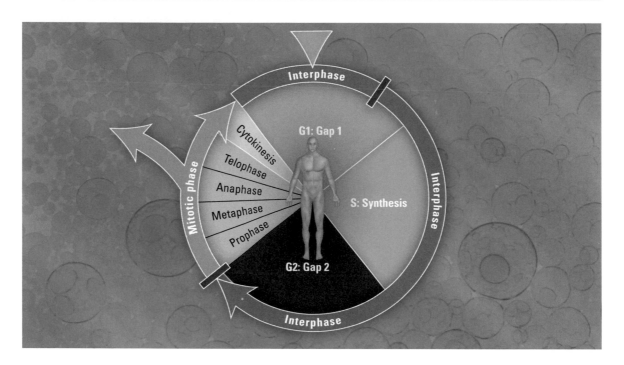

Figure 5.1 The Eukaryotic Cell Cycle.

All eukaryotic cells exist at some point in the cell cycle, which is the order of events in the life of a cell. The cell cycle consists of large phases called interphase and the mitotic phase, each of which contains smaller phases within them. Interphase contains the G_1 (first gap), S (synthesis), and G_2 (second gap) phases, and the mitotic phase consists of prophase, metaphase, anaphase, and telophase, and ends with cytokinesis, the final splitting of the cell.

The G_1 phase of interphase is what occurs when the cell has just formed after mitosis and cytokinesis. During this time the cell is very actively growing in size and adding organelles and other necessary molecules. The S phase of interphase is when the DNA of the cell, which is arranged into chromosomes, is copied in preparation for mitosis. Upon copy, the homologous chromosomes are called sister chromatids and are attached at a centromere. The G_2 phase of interphase occurs as the cell is further preparing for division. During this time the cell copies more organelles, the chromosomes begin to condense into distinct compact structures, and the cell increases in size.

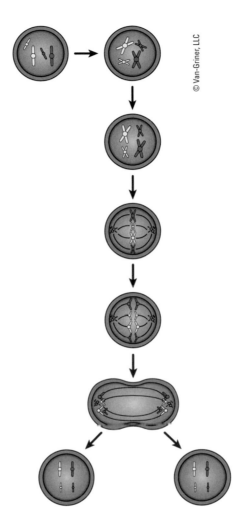

© Van-Griner, LLC

Figure 5.2 Mitosis. Animal cell undergoing mitosis and cytokinesis.

The mitotic phase of the cell cycle consists of the stages prophase, metaphase, anaphase, and telophase, which is when the sister chromatids are separated and new nuclei form, and cytokinesis, which is the final separation of the cytoplasm into two new cells. During prophase the chromosomes, which as you recall now consist of two attached copies called sister chromatids, further condense into structures that are visible with the light microscope. The nucleus of the cell begins to break down, and spindle fibers begin to grow out from the centrosomes toward the center of the cell. In metaphase, the nucleus has completely broken down and spindle fibers are attached to each pair of sister chromatids at the centromere. The pulling of the spindle fibers aligns the chromosomes, still attached as sister chromosomes, along the middle of the cell, often called the equatorial or metaphase plate. In anaphase, the spindle fibers pull the sister chromatids apart towards opposite ends of the cell, separating them into what are now called daughter chromosomes. The action of the spindle fibers also cause the cell to elongate. Finally, in telophase, the two sets of chromosomes are now at opposite ends of the cell, new nuclei begin to form, and the spindle fibers disappear. Also, at this time a cleavage furrow begins to form around the cell, signaling the beginning of cytokinesis. Lastly, cytokinesis, the division of the cytoplasm, occurs, and two new cells are formed, each of which is now in the G_1 phase of interphase.

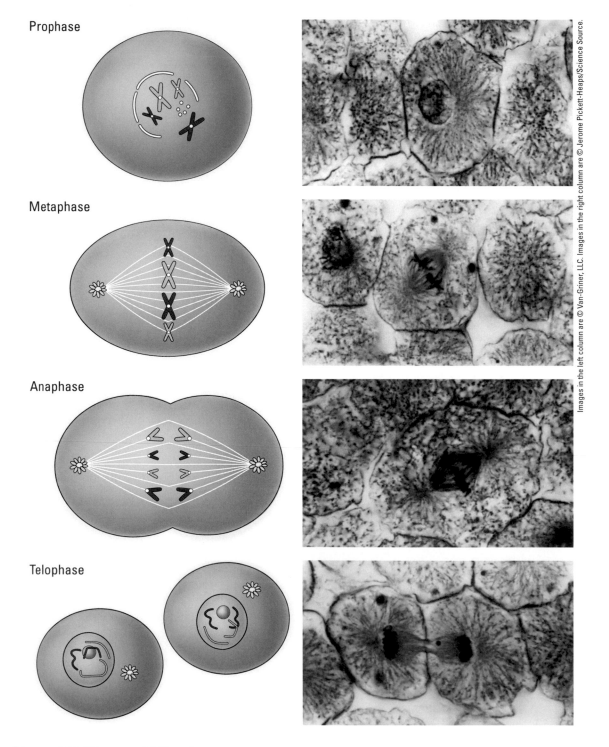

Figure 5.3 Stages of Mitosis.

An important difference occurs during mitosis in plant cells due the presence of a rigid cell wall surrounding the cell. Plant cells do not form a cleavage furrow as animal cells do, but instead a section of cell wall, called a cell plate, forms between the newly formed cells, separating them into two new cells.

Meiosis is a special type of cell division which occurs in certain cells of sexually reproducing organisms. It is important for the process of gametogenesis, which produces the gametes, or sex cells. It is important to remember that most eukaryotic organisms are diploid ($2n$), meaning their cells have two copies of each chromosome, whereas gametes are haploid ($1n$) and contain only one copy of each chromosome. This is necessary so that when two haploid gametes fuse during fertilization, the diploid condition is restored in the resulting zygote. For example, humans have 46 total chromosomes in most of our cells, which is the diploid ($2n$) condition. This means we have 23 pairs, or homologues, of each chromosome 1 through 23 in these cells. Meiosis reduces this so that each gamete produced has only one copy of each chromosome, which is the haploid ($1n$) condition.

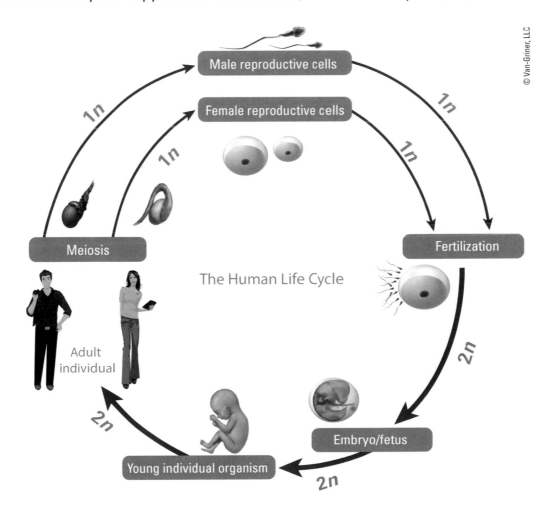

© Van-Griner, LLC

Figure 5.4 Human Life Cycle.

Meiosis resembles mitosis in many ways, but there are important differences. First of all meiosis consists of two stages, meiosis I and meiosis II, each of which has a prophase, metaphase, anaphase and telophase, and called prophase I, metaphase I, and so on. Another important difference is that the chromosomes are copied one time, but separated twice. This means that after the process of meiosis, one diploid (2*n*) cell has produced four haploid (1*n*) cells.

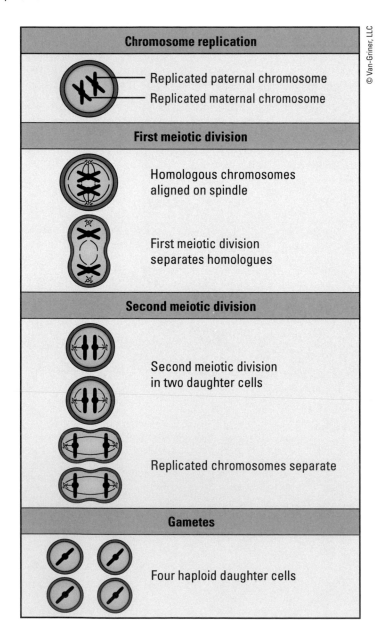

Figure 5.5 Stages of Meiosis. The process of meiosis, the type of cell division necessary for sexual reproduction in eukaryotes. The cells produced by meiosis are gametes or spores.

It is also important to understand the ways in which meiosis maintains and adds to genetic diversity through sexual reproduction. One of these ways is through independent assortment of the chromosomes, which means that the way in which the homologous chromosomes are separated into the gametes is random, and every resulting gamete can have any combination of maternal and paternal homologues.

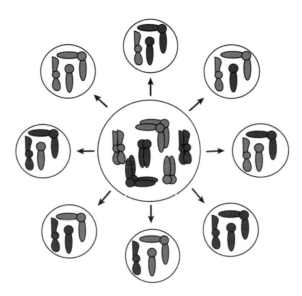

Figure 5.6 Independent Assortment.

The second way is through crossing over, which occurs during prophase I of meiosis I. During this process, the now duplicated homologous chromosomes line up next to one another, and sections of them switch with each other. The result is a shuffling of the genes between the maternal and paternal homologues and the production of brand new combinations of genes on the chromosomes.

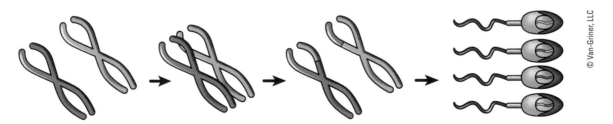

© Van-Griner, LLC

Figure 5.7 Crossing Over. Gene Recombination: Crossing over between the homologous chromosomes during spermatogenesis meiosis.

LAB ACTIVITIES

ANIMAL CELL MITOSIS

1. Obtain a slide of whitefish blastula mitosis. This slide contains cells from an early embryo and as such contains cells that were very actively dividing.

2. With your lab partner, look at the slide and identify all of the different stages of mitosis, paying close attention to the chromosomes and their activity.

3. Can you see what the chromosomes are doing in each stage? You will likely need to move the slide around and look at different sections of the embryo to find the different stages.

4. As you examine the cells do sketches of each of the stages.

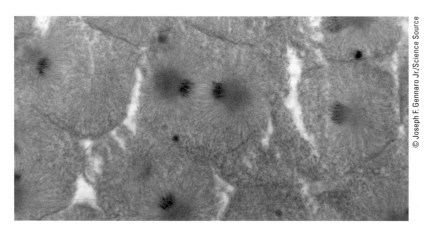

© Joseph F. Gennaro Jr./Science Source

Figure 5.8 Whitefish Cells Undergoing Mitosis. Light micrograph of whitefish cells in anaphase stage of mitosis. Mitosis is the cell division of a nucleus, typically consisting of four stages: prophase, metaphase, anaphase, and telophase. During anaphase, chromosomes move to opposite poles of the cell. Magnification 160× at 35 mm.

PLANT CELL MITOSIS

1. Obtain a slide of an onion root tip. This slide contains stained cells from the root of an onion that were actively dividing as the root pushed through the soil.

2. With your lab partner, look at the slide and identify the different stages of mitosis in the onion cells.

3. Look specifically for ways in which the shape of the cell differs in these cells versus the mitosis in the whitefish.

4. Identify the cell plate in cells finishing mitosis and cytokinesis and make sketches of what you see.

Figure 5.9 Onion Root Tip Mitosis. Light micrograph of an onion (*Allium cepa*) root tip, showing different phases of mitosis. Active cell nucleuses can be seen. In the middle, chromosomes are in the anaphase, when the chromatids pull apart. To the left of it are disentangled chromosomes in prophase. The surrounding cell nucleuses are mainly in the incipient division stage, the interphase. Magnification 630×.

OBSERVATION OF MEIOSIS

1. Obtain a slide of a *lilium* ovary. This will contain plant cells undergoing meiosis for the purpose of sexual reproduction.

2. With your lab partner, and using prepared images as a guide, attempt to identify the different stages of meiosis.

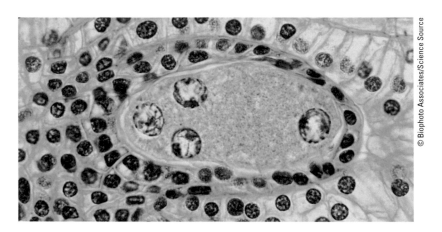

Figure 5.10 *Lilium* Ovary. Light Micrograph (LM) of a longitudinal section of embryo sac in transverse section of ovary of Lily *(Lilium)*. Three nuclei migrate to one end. All show prophases of next divisions (mitosis). Magnification 250× at 6 cm.

OBSERVATION OF MATURE GAMETES

1. Obtain slides of mature sperm and cat ovary sections.

2. With your lab partner, look at the cat ovary section and identify the developing ovarian follicles. These contain oocytes in varying degrees of maturity. Sketch what you see.

3. Observe the slide of mature sperm. Make sure to identify the different sections, such as the head, acrosome, and tail. Sketch what you see.

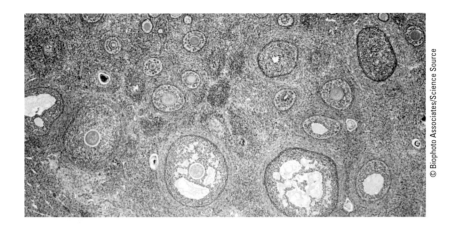

Figure 5.11 Developing Ovarian Follicles. Light micrograph of developing ovarian follicles in rabbit (longitudinal section).

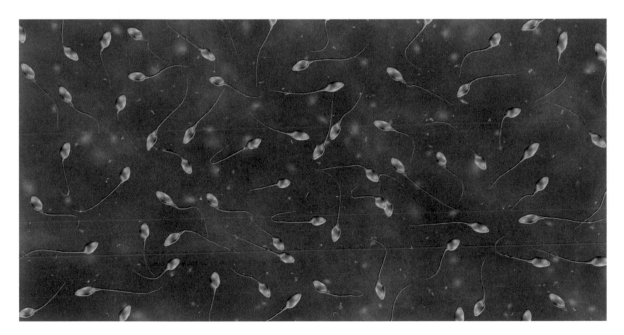

Figure 5.12 Human Sperm. Light micrograph (LM) of human sperm with counterstaining.

NOTES

Biology 101 Laboratory Manual

LABORATORY 5 REVIEW
MITOSIS: CELL REPRODUCTION, AND
MEIOSIS: SEXUAL REPRODUCTION

QUESTIONS

MITOSIS

1. Explain the difference between interphase and mitosis.

   _____

   _____

   _____

2. What are the functions of mitosis, and why is it so important for unicellular and multicellular organisms?

   _____

   _____

   _____

3. Prior to a cell entering mitosis the DNA must be duplicated in the S phase of interphase. Why is this so important?

_____

_____

_____

4. What is the function of the spindle fibers during mitosis?

_____

_____

_____

5. What is cytokinesis?

_____

_____

_____

6. What is the difference between mitosis in animal cells and plant cells?

_____

_____

_____

7. Are the resulting cells in mitosis identical or different from the parent cell? Explain.

_____

_____

_____

MEIOSIS

1. Why is meiosis important for sexually reproducing animals?

   _____

   _____

   _____

   _____

2. What are homologous chromosomes? Explain.

   _____

   _____

   _____

   _____

3. Define the terms haploid and diploid and explain what they mean in terms of chromosome numbers.

   _____

   _____

   _____

   _____

4. Why are crossing over and independent assortment important in producing and maintaining genetic diversity?

   _____

   _____

   _____

   _____

5. If a cell entering meiosis (after multiplication of the DNA in interphase) has 36 chromosomes, how many chromosomes will exist in each nucleus when meiosis concludes?

_____

_____

_____

_____

6. Why is meiosis referred to as a reduction division?

_____

_____

_____

_____

7. What are the names of female and male gametes? Are they haploid or diploid? What is a zygote? Is a zygote haploid or diploid?

_____

_____

_____

_____

8. Are the resulting cells (daughter cells) of meiosis identical or different from the parent cell? Explain.

_____

_____

_____

_____

LABORATORY 6
GENETICS

LEARNING OBJECTIVES

- Understand Mendelian Genetics, Particulate Theory, Law of Segregation, and Law of Independent Assortment.

- Summarize basic genetic terminology.

- Set up and solve monohybrid Punnett squares.

- Have an understanding of basic genetic situations such as co-dominance and ABO blood typing, incomplete dominance, and lethal inheritance.

- Distinguish between basic genetic human traits and some human diseases that are caused by genetic traits.

INTRODUCTION

Before the mid 1800s, the mechanism on how individuals receive their genetic characteristics was not understood. Oftentimes a "Blending Theory of Inheritance" was considered the best explanation on how an organism receives its characteristics, such as height or fur color. The blending theory stated that characteristics of an individual are averaged or blended from their parents. For example, if a tall person and a short person procreated, their offspring would be of medium height. It wasn't until an Austrian monk named Gregor Mendel shed some light on how traits are inherited from a parent to its offspring. Mendel studied garden pea plants in his genetic experiments because they were easy to fertilize and had a quicker reproduction rate than many organisms. Mendel's experiments were the foundation of what is known today as Mendelian genetics.

Figure 6.1 Gregor Johann Mendel. Gregor Johann Mendel (July 20, 1822–January 6, 1884) was an Austrian scientist and Augustinian friar who gained posthumous fame as the founder of the new science of genetics.

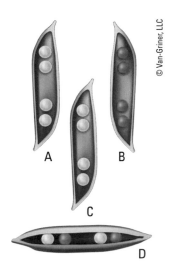

Figure 6.2 Mendel's Peas. Gregor Mendel (1822–1884) cross-bred peas that produced yellow (A) and green (B) peas. This produces a generation in which the peas are yellow (C). This is because the color of the peas is controlled by an allele in which yellow color is dominant. An allele is a pair of genes that have different effects on the same characteristic, for instance controlling pea color. By breeding the C generation peas together, Mendel found that the next generation had a mixture of pea colors (D). The ratio of yellow to green peas was 3:1. His work formed the basis of genetic theory.

Mendel's Particulate Theory replaced the Blending Theory of Inheritance. The Particulate Theory states

1. Inherited characters are determined by certain factors, which are now known to be genes.

2. These genes occur in pairs. One set originates from maternal chromosomes and the other from paternal chromosomes.

3. Traits are determined in an individual according to the two copies of genes an individual inherits from its parents' gametes.

These postulates are known as the **Law of Segregation** (or Mendel's 1st Law). Mendel's 2nd Law, known as the **Law of Independent Assortment** states that the genes on different or non-homologous chromosomes will be distributed randomly into gametes such as the sperm and egg.

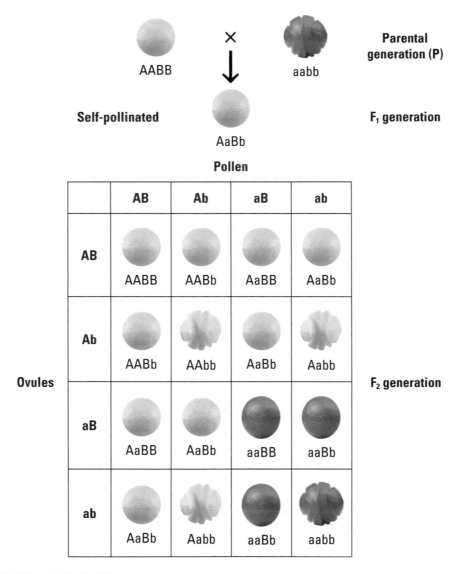

Figure 6.3 Mendel's 2nd Law. Law of Independent Assortment.

There are many terms associated with genetics and it is very important to become familiar with them before studying genetics further:

- **Alleles**—Alternative versions of a gene that are found in pairs on chromosomes (i.e., tall or short).

- **Dominant**—Alleles that mask the expression of other alleles and are represented by a capital letter (tall or T).

- **Recessive**—Alleles whose expression is masked by a dominant allele and is represented by a lowercase letter (short or t).

- **Genotype**—Alleles that are present with in an organism's chromosomes (TT, Tt, or tt).

- **Phenotype**—Alleles that are physically expressed in an organism (tall or short).

- **Homozygous**—When paired alleles are the same (TT or tt).

- **Heterozygous**—When paired alleles are different (Tt).

SIMPLE DOMINANCE AND PUNNETT SQUARES

Simple Dominance is when a single gene codes for a particular trait such as flower pigment. Mendel crossed red colored flowering plants with white flowering plants. The red flowered plants were dominant to white flowers therefore, masking the expression of the white flowers. These white flowering plants are considered recessive. Only when the white flowers were homozygous, the white phenotype is expressed. A Punnett square is an easy tool used to determine what offspring will occur when two parents' alleles are established into offspring.

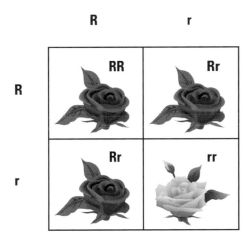

Figure 6.4 Punnett Square of Simple Dominance.

HUMAN GENETIC DISEASES

- **Galactosemia**—Inherited as an autosomal recessive trait, Galactosemia causes an individual to be unable to metabolize (or digest) galactose, a sugar that is commonly found in milk. About five cases occur per million births.

- **Cystic fibrosis**—A recessive trait that causes chronic brachial obstruction through thick mucus secretions and growth impairments.

- **Juvenile retinoblastoma**—Disease is caused by a recessive gene and is found on chromosome 13. Juvenile retinoblastoma causes cancer of the retina at a young age.

- **Muscular dystrophy**—Sex linked disease in which there is a mutation on the X chromosome. Dystrophin, an important protein in skeletal muscle formation is no produced properly and causes a variety of muscular impairments.

- **Phenylketonuria**—Inherited by a recessive gene and often referred to as PKU. Phenylketonuria occurs approximately in 100 of 1 million births. PKU prevents the amino acid phenylalanine from being metabolized. If left untreated developmental delays can occur.

- **Huntington's disease**—Caused by a dominant trait and generally occurs later in life. Huntington's is a neurodegenerative disorder that inhibits muscle coordination and eventually leads to cognitive decline and behavioral symptoms. Unfortunately, because Huntington's symptoms appear later in life, a sufferer often has children who have a 50% chance to become affected by the disease because it is a dominant trait.

- **Tay Sac's disease**—Tay Sac's is a rare autosomal recessive disease. Symptoms are caused by a progressive deterioration of nerve cells beginning at around six months of age and usually results in death by age four.

LAB ACTIVITIES

PUNNETT SQUARES AND SIMPLE DOMINANCE

1. Set up a Punnett square for crossing a homozygous purple (PP) with a homozygous white (pp) flowering plant (see Figure 6.4 for set-up).

   a. What are the offspring's genotypes?

   _____

   _____

   b. What are the offspring's phenotypes?

   _____

   _____

2. The first generation of the plants' offspring is known as the F_1 generation (or 1st generation) ... Now cross two of the offspring from the F_1 generation to determine the offspring of the F_2 generation (or 2nd generation).

a. What are the F_2 generation genotypes?

_____

_____

b. What are the F_2 generation phenotypes?

_____

_____

GENOTYPES AND PHENOTYPES FOR ALBINISM

Albinism is a homozygous recessive condition found in many animals in which melanin is not produced, causing little or no pigment in the skin, hair, and eyes. If a female giraffe having normal coloring (AA) mates with a male albino giraffe (aa), what are the following genotypic and phenotypic ratios?

Figure 6.5 Albino Giraffe versus Normal Color Giraffe.

a. What is the genotype of mother giraffe?

_____

_____

b. What is the genotype of father giraffe?

_____

_____

c. What are the possible gametes of mother (remember each individual is diploid, having two gametes)?

_____

_____

d. What are the possible gametes of father?

_____

_____

e. What is the possible offspring?

_____

_____

f. What is the genetic ratio of offspring?

_____

_____

g. What is the phenotypic ratio of offspring?

_____

_____

OBSERVE CORN PLANT GENETICS

1. Look at the short and tall corn plants and the albino and normal pigmented corn plants provided by your instructor.

2. Observe the monohybrid and di-hybrid crosses of the corn kernels. The **monohybrid cross** involves only one trait (such as corn kernel color). **Di-hybrid crosses** involve two traits (kernel color and smooth/wrinkled kernels). Can you determine any genotypic frequencies by looking at the corn plants?

Figure 6.6 Young Corn Plant.

Figure 6.7 Bi-Colored Corn. Corn (*Zea mays*) with seeds showing F₁ ratios. The ratio of white kernels to purple kernels is 3 to 1.

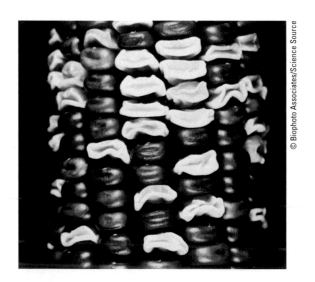

Figure 6.8 Di-Hybrid Cross. Corn (*Zea mays*) with seeds showing F₁ ratios. This cob demonstrates two-point linkage—the red kernels are smooth, and the yellow kernels are shrunken. There are no smooth yellow kernels or shrunken red kernels.

3. Observe Transposons. **Transposons** are fragments of DNA that are inserted in corn to produce white and yellow corn that we find in the supermarket. This insertion of DNA does not allow for the production of a purple pigment. Indian corn is corn that does not have this transposon or DNA inserted into it. Depending on when and what type of DNA fragment is inserted, various colors can be produced in the corn kernels. Observe some various ears of corn, including Indian corn in lab.

4. Observe Lethal Inheritance. **Lethal Inheritance** is a genetic condition that kills the offspring. An example of lethal inheritance is albino corn plants. Albino corn plants will die as soon as the nutrients in their seed and the soil around them run out. These plants lack chlorophyll, the green pigment found in chloroplasts. Chlorophyll is a necessary component of photosynthesis and without it the corn plant is unable to produce enough energy to survive.

Figure 6.9 Albino Corn Plant.

PHENOTYPES AND GENOTYPES OF HUMAN TRAITS

Many traits are determined by a single gene. In the table below list your phenotype and your genotype (if you know it) and compare with the rest of the students at your lab bench.

Table 6.1 Traits.

Characteristics	Phenotype	Genotype	Notes
Freckles			
Widow's Peak			
Bent Little Finger			
PTC Tasting			
Hitchhiker's Thumb			
Cleft Chin			
Attached Earlobes			
Pigmented Iris			
Six Fingers			
Mid-digital Hair			
Interlacing Fingers			

- **Freckles**—Freckles are clusters of concentrated melanin and their presence occurrence is due to a single gene. The presence of freckles is dominant, F, and the absence is recessive, f.

- **Widow's peak**—A pointed hairline (think Dracula) is the dominant allele, W. A straight hairline is recessive, w.

© By United States Congress [Public domain or Public domain], via Wikimedia Commons from Wikimedia Commons. https://commons. wikimedia.org/wiki/File%3APaul_Ryan%2C_official_portrait%2C_112th_ Congress_2.jpg

Figure 6.10 Widow's Peak.

- **Bent little finger**—When placing relaxed hands on a flat surface, if the last joint of your pinkie finger points inward towards the rest of your hand you have the dominant allele, B. If your little finger remains straight, you possess the recessive allele, b.

- **PTC tasting**—PTC stands for phenylthiocarbamide. Depending on your genetic makeup it will taste bitter or virtually tasteless. The bitter taste indicates a dominant allele or T. A similar phenomenon has been found in individuals who find vegetables such as broccoli bitter tasting, but that is controlled by differing genes.

■ **Hitchhiker's thumb**—If you can bend your thumb backwards 60° or more you have the recessive allele, h, or hitchhiker's thumb.

Figure 6.11 Hitchhiker's Thumb.

Figure 6.12 Normal Thumb.

■ **Cleft or dimpled chin**—Cleft chin is the dominant allele, or M.

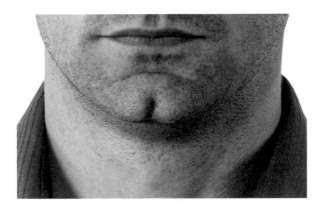

Figure 6.13 Cleft Chin.

■ **Attached earlobes**—Unattached earlobes, or A, is the dominant allele and is recessive to attached earlobes, a.

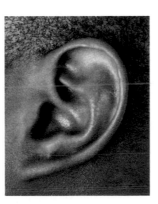

Figure 6.14 Attached Earlobe.

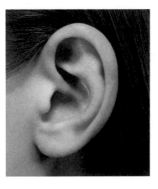

Figure 6.15 Unattached Earlobes.

- **Pigmented iris**—If you have either blue or gray eyes you do not produce pigment in the front layer of your iris. Blue and gray eye color is a recessive trait, or p. If you produce pigment in the front layer of your iris and have green, hazel, brown, or black eyes, you carry the dominant allele, P.

- **Six fingers**—In humans, having six fingers is actually a dominant allele, S. However, this allele is not found frequently among the human population. Most individuals are homozygous recessive, ss, and only have five fingers on each hand.

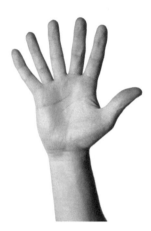

Figure 6.16 Six Fingers.

- **Mid-digital hair**—M is the allele for hair on the middle segments of fingers. The allele for no hair on the mid-digits is m.

- **Interlacing fingers**—When you casually fold your hands and interlace your fingers, if your left thumb crosses over your right thumb you have the dominant allele, C. If your right thumb crosses over your left you have the recessive allele, c.

INCOMPLETE DOMINANCE

Incomplete dominance occurs when the heterozygous genotype does not take on the dominant allele but is intermediate between the dominant and recessive phenotypes. This often happens in plant or flower genetics. An example of this is found in flowers such as snapdragons or carnations, R is the dominant phenotype and is red, r is recessive and is white in color. The homozygous dominant (RR) has a red phenotype and the homozygous recessive (rr) has a white phenotype. Heterozygous genotype Rr is pink in color (a mixture between red and white), and is, therefore, incompletely dominant.

Figure 6.17 Incomplete Dominance in Snapdragons (rr, RR, and Rr). A digital composite image showing three colors of snapdragon (Antirrhinum majus) which are an example of the principle of incomplete dominance in genetics. When red and white snapdragons are crossed, the all-heterozygous offspring of the F_1 generation are all pink. The F_2 generation has all three colors, but in a ratio of 1:2:1 as opposed to the 3:1 ratio seen where there is complete dominance.

1. If a red carnation (RR) is crossed with a white carnation (rr) What are the offspring's genotypes and phenotypes of the F_1 generation?

a. What are the F_1 generation genotypes?

_____

_____

b. What are the F_1 generation phenotypes?

_____

_____

2. If two of the offspring from the F_1 generation are crossed, what are the genotypes and phenotypes of the F_2 generation?

<table>
<tr><td></td><td></td></tr>
<tr><td></td><td></td></tr>
</table>

a. What are the F_2 generation genotypes?

_____

_____

b. What are the F_2 generation phenotypes?

_____

_____

CO-DOMINANCE AND ABO BLOOD TYPING

Co-dominance is when two alleles both contribute to a phenotype equally. Blood typing is an example of this. Blood typing is determined by the presence or absence of antigens found on red blood cells. There are two types of antigens A or B. Individuals with A antigens are type A and those with B antigens on their red blood cells are type B. Individuals with both A and B antigens are type AB. The A and B antigens are co-dominant with each other; neither is dominant over the other. Lastly, the absence of A and B antigens are ABO blood type O. The allele for type O blood, "i" is recessive to A and B alleles (I^A and I^B, respectively).

The particular antigens present on the surface of the red blood cells determines the antibodies found in the blood's plasma. These antibodies make certain blood types not compatible with each other. For example, type A has anti-B antibodies in its plasma and an individual with type B has anti-A antibodies in their plasma. If A and B blood mix (such as during a blood transfusion) the antibodies will attack the antigens found on the blood cell and agglutinate (or stick together). These agglutination reactions cause blood to clump and to not flow properly and also cause toxic reactions that could kill an individual.

Type AB individuals do not carry any antibodies in their plasma making them the universal blood recipients. Type O has both anti-A and anti-B antibodies in their blood plasma. Type O is considered the universal donor, despite having both anti-bodies in their plasma. This is because when blood is donated, the cellular portion of the blood (the red and white blood cells) is used and the plasma portion containing the antibodies is discarded. If plasma is being donated, only the plasma portion of the blood is being donated and the cellular portion is given back to the donor during the process.

The Rh factor is indicated by the + or − sign after your ABO blood type. The Rh factor was first discovered in the Rhesus monkey and is another antigen on the red blood cell. Those with the Rh antigen are Rh+ and individuals without the Rh antigen are Rh−. Rh− blood does have the capacity to make antibodies against Rh+ blood and therefore is not considered compatible with Rh+ blood.

Figure 6.18 Red Blood Cells. Red blood cells which are involved in delivering oxygen to the body.

Table 6.2 ABO Blood Group System.

	A	B	AB		0	
Red Blood Cell Type						
Antigens Present	Antigen A	Antigen B	Antigen A and B		None	
Antibodies Present	Antibody B	Antibody A	None		Antibody A and B	
Genotype	$I^A i$ $I^A I^A$	AO AA	$I^B i$ $I^B I^B$	BO BB	$I^A I^B$	AB	i i	OO
Can Receive Blood From	A or O		B or O		A, B, AB, or O		O	

Surface Antigens + Opposing Antibodies → Agglutination (clumping) and Hemolysis

Figure 6.19 Rhesus Monkeys (*Macaca mulatta*). Female Rhesus monkey with its young. This monkey is also called Rhesus macaque.

CRIME SCENE INVESTIGATION

Participate in a crime scene investigation with the Wards' Whodunit Activity provided by your lab instructor.

Biology 101 Laboratory Manual

LABORATORY 6 REVIEW
GENETICS

QUESTIONS

1. Explain Mendel's Law of Segregation in your own words.

   _____

   _____

2. Explain Mendel's Law of Independent Assortment in your own words.

   _____

   _____

3. What is the difference between phenotype and genotype?

   _____

   _____

4. Is it possible to determine the genotype of an individual having a dominant phenotype?

_____

_____

_____

5. A heterozygous tall plant (Tt) is crossed with a homozygous recessive short plant (tt). Set up a Punnett square and determine what are the probable genotypes and phenotypes of their offspring.

_____

_____

_____

6. An albino man marries a female who is of normal pigmentation, but has an albino mother. Set up a Punnett square and determine what are the probable genotypes and phenotypes of their offspring.

_____

_____

_____

7. In incomplete dominance, a heterozygous (Rr) carnation is crossed with a white (rr) carnation. What are the genotypes and phenotypes of the offspring? Explain the heterozygous phenotype in incomplete dominance.

_____

_____

_____

8. What is a widow's peak? If a person has a widow's peak, what is their genotype?

_____

_____

_____

NAME: _____ DATE:_____

9. Explain lethal inheritance in corn plants. Can lethal inheritance remain in a population if a homozygous recessive albino corn plant is crossed with a normal corn plant? Why or why not?

_____

_____

_____

10. What is a dihybrid cross? Give an example.

_____

_____

_____

11. Explain co-dominance. How is blood genetics co-dominant?

_____

_____

_____

12. What blood types are not expected for children to have if their parents have AB blood? O blood?

_____

_____

_____

13. How can type O blood be used as a universal donor when its plasma contains anti-A and anti-B antibodies?

_____

_____

_____

14. If a mother has A blood and a father has B blood, is it possible for them to have a child that has O blood? Complete a Punnett square and show your work.

_____

_____

_____

15. What determines the phenotypes found in a population? Can the phenotypes change or shift from generation to generation?

_____

_____

_____

LABORATORY 7
BIOTECHNOLOGY

LEARNING OBJECTIVES

- Identify the components and structure of DNA.

- Describe gene expression, including the synthesis of DNA, RNA, and protein.

- Isolate DNA from cheek cells.

- Use gel electrophoresis to separate a mixture of DNA fragments.

- Determine the length of a fragment of DNA.

INTRODUCTION

Biotechnology is the isolation and manipulation of biologically important molecules (DNA, RNA, protein) for the purpose of understanding their structure and function and then altering their structure to improve their function. This lab has three parts: to review the structure and synthesis of DNA, RNA, and protein; to isolate DNA from cheek cells; and to determine the length of a piece of DNA using gel electrophoresis and comparing its migration to the migration of pieces of DNA of known length.

DNA stands for deoxyribonucleic acid. It is the genetic material in the cell. In eukaryotic cells it is found in the nucleus; in prokaryotic cells it is found in the cytoplasm since there is no nucleus. DNA in both types of cells is a polymer made of monomers called nucleotides. Each nucleotide consists of a 5-carbon sugar called deoxyribose, at least one phosphate group, and a base containing nitrogen, carbon, and oxygen. There are four different bases in DNA. Adenine (A) and guanine (G) are purines with two rings. Cytosine (C) and thymine (T) are pyrimidines with one ring. The DNA exists as a double helix or twisted ladder. The sugars and phosphate groups are on the outside forming a sugar-phosphate backbone with the bases pointing inward forming the "rungs" of the "ladder." The bases of one helix are hydrogen-bonded to the bases in the other helix. Adenine is always bonded to thymine and guanine is always bonded to cytosine. This is called "complementary base pairing," and it maintains the same width of the DNA molecule for its entire length.

Figure 7.1 DNA Double Helix.

DNA REPLICATION

The complementary base pairing of the two strands of DNA in the double helix not only provides uniform geometry for what can be very long molecules but also informs the synthesis of new DNA. The synthesis of new DNA is called replication, because it is important that new DNA is exactly like the existing DNA. The enzyme that makes the new strands of DNA is called DNA polymerase. Each strand of nucleotides serves as a template or guide for the synthesis of a new, complementary strand. Each new double helix consists of one "old" strand and one "new" strand of nucleotides. This is called "semiconservative replication."

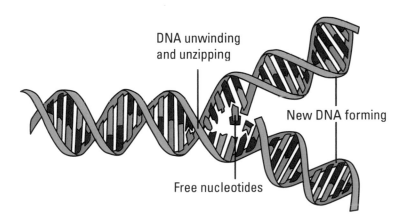

DNA unwinding and unzipping

New DNA forming

Free nucleotides

Figure 7.2 Transcription.

REPLICATION EXERCISE

Below is a strand of DNA. Supply the complementary strand.

T A C G G G C A A C T C T G G C T A A A C A G A A A A

__ __

RNA STRUCTURE AND SYNTHESIS

RNA stands for ribonucleic acid. It is also a polymer made of monomers called nucleotides. In RNA nucleotides, the 5-carbon sugar is ribose and the four bases are adenine, guanine, cytosine, and uracil. There are several types of RNA in the cell. Ribosomal RNA (rRNA) is part of the ribosome. Transfer RNA (tRNA) is important in protein synthesis (translation). Messenger RNA (mRNA) carries the directions for making a protein from the DNA to the ribosomes. The process by which RNA is made is called transcription. The RNA is complementary to one of the strands of DNA in the double helix. In eukaryotic cells, it is made in the nucleus and then travels to the cytoplasm. The enzyme RNA polymerase unzips part of the DNA double helix, reads the sequence of bases, recruits nucleotides with complementary bases, and joins the sugars and phosphates together. In eukaryotes, RNA is made in the nucleus and then travels to the cytoplasm where the ribosomes will use the code to make proteins.

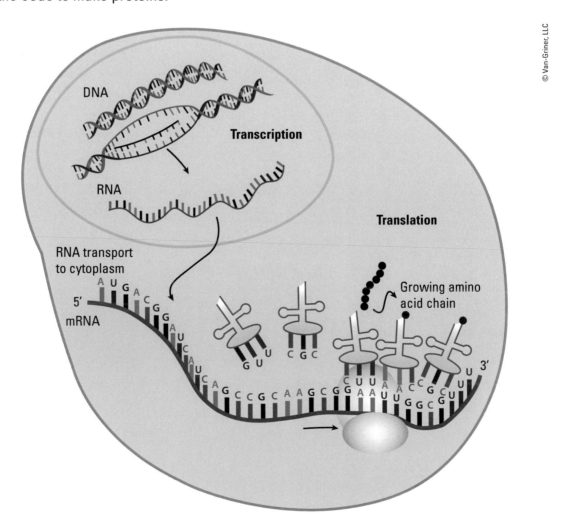

© Van-Griner, LLC

Figure 7.3 rRNA Transcription.

PROTEIN STRUCTURE AND SYNTHESIS

Proteins are polymers made of amino acid monomers. Proteins are made by ribosomes in a process called translation. Ribosomes read the directions in the mRNA, recruit the appropriate tRNA carrying an amino acid, and join the amino acids together. The ribosomes read three bases in the mRNA at a time. The three bases are called a "codon," and the genetic code is called a triplet code because of these groups of three bases. The ribosome recruits a tRNA molecule with an anticodon complementary to the codon, or group of three nucleotides in the mRNA. Each tRNA carries an amino acid, and the ribosome joins the amino acids together according to the order of bases in the mRNA molecule.

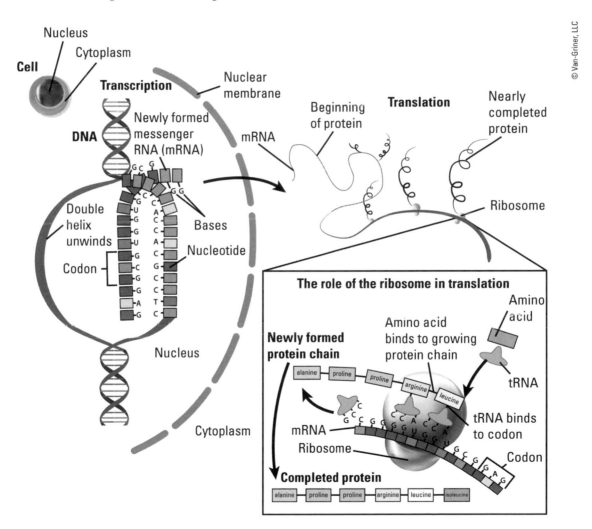

Figure 7.4 mRNA Transcription.

Table 7.3 The Genetic Code.

First Letter	Second Letter								Third Letter
	U		C		A		G		
U	UUU	Phe Phenylala-nine	UCU	Ser Serine	UAU	Tyr Tyrosine	UGU	Cys Cysteine	U
	UUC		UCC		UAC		UGC		C
	UUA	Leu Leucine	UCA		UAA	STOP	UGA	STOP	A
	UUG		UCG		UAG		UGG	Trp Tryptophan	G
C	CUU	Leu Leucine	CCU	Pro Proline	CAU	His Histidine	CGU	Arg Arginine	U
	CUC		CCC		CAC		CGC		C
	CUA		CCA		CAA	Gln Glutamine	CGA		A
	CUG		CCG		CAG		CGG		G
A	AUU	Ile Isoleucine	ACU	Thr Threonine	AAU	Asn Asparagine	AGU	Ser Serine	U
	AUC		ACC		AAC		AGC		C
	AUA	Met Methionine	ACA		AAA	Lys Lysine	AGA	Arg Arginine	A
	AUG		ACG		AAG		AGG		G
G	GUU	Val Valine	GCU	Ala Alanine	GAU	Asp Aspartic Acid	GGU	Gly Glycine	U
	GUC		GCC		GAC		GGC		C
	GUA		GCA		GAA	Glu Glutamic Acid	GGA		A
	GUG		GCG		GAG		GGG		G

GENE EXPRESSION EXERCISE:

T A C G G G C A A C T C T G G C T A A A C A G A A A A

mRNA codons

— —

tRNA anticodons

— —

Amino acids

_____   _____   _____   _____   _____   _____   _____   _____   _____

GEL ELECTROPHORESIS

Gel electrophoresis is a technique that separates molecules based on size and charge. The electrophoresis chamber has electrodes (wires) at either end. The wires can be attached to a power supply. The chamber is filled with a buffer containing salt. The buffer maintains the pH of the solution at slightly above seven. In this basic pH, the phosphate groups in the DNA backbone are negatively charged. The salt conducts electricity.

A gel is made of agarose, a sugar extracted from the cell walls of red algae. The agarose come as a powder. The powder is heated in buffer (like Jell-O®), and the molten agarose is poured into a plastic mold. A comb is inserted into the agarose before it hardens so that when it sets there will be indentations or wells. The gel is placed into the electrophoresis chamber and covered with buffer.

A mixture of DNA fragments of known size is added to a well on the gel. Another well is filled with a sample of DNA containing a fragment of unknown size. The DNA runs on the gel for about 45 minutes. The gel is stained, and the distance that each piece of DNA ran is measured. The size (in base pairs) of the unknown piece of DNA can be calculated by comparing the distance it migrated with the distance the pieces of DNA of known size migrated. The distances that the DNA fragments of known size are plotted on a graph using semi-log paper, and a best-fit line is drawn through those points. The distance that the unknown piece of DNA migrated is also plotted on the graph, and its place on the line is used to determine its length.

ISOLATION OF CHEEK CELL DNA

In eukaryotic cells, such as your cheek cells, the DNA is located in the nucleus. In order to extract the DNA, the cell must be ruptured. This is done with detergent that pokes holes in the phospholipid bilayers of both the plasma membrane and the nuclear envelope. The DNA must be maintained in the proper salt concentration, and the electrolytes in the Gatorade® provide these. Alcohol causes the DNA to come out of solution (precipitate).

LAB ACTIVITIES

GEL ELECTROPHORESIS

1. Obtain an agarose gel from your instructor and place it in the electrophoresis chamber. Each chamber can hold four gels. Cover the gels with buffer.

2. Using a micropipettor, add 12 µl of DNA markers to one well. Add 12 µl of unknown DNA to a second well. Add 12 µl of dye markers to a third well.

3. Put the top on the electrophoresis chamber, connect the electrodes to the power supply, set the power supply to 170 volts, and turn it on. Make sure that current is going through the chamber.

4. Allow the gel to run for about 45 minutes to an hour. Turn off the power; disconnect the wires from the power supply. If the orange band is within two inches of the bottom, the gel has finished running.

5. Stain and destain the gel according to the directions given in lab. Observe the gel on a light box.

6. Using the clear plastic rulers, measure the distance in cm from the well to each band.

7. The lengths of the marker DNA in kilobase pairs is as follows: 23.1, 9.4, 6.7, 4.4, 2.3, 2.0.

8. Plot the points of the marker DNA on the semi-log paper provided. Draw a best-fit line using the four smaller bands.

9. Determine the length of the unknown fragment of DNA by finding the distance migrated on the x-axis, going up to the line, and then determining its length in base pairs by going over to the y-axis.

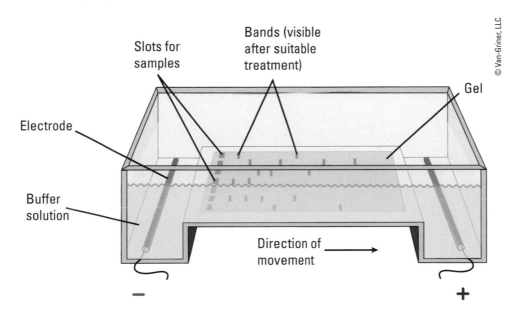

Figure 7.5 Agarose Gel Electrophoresis of DNA.

ISOLATION OF CHEEK CELL DNA

(Prior to the start of this exercise, spit out any gum. Cheek cells stick to gum.)

1. Obtain a large test tube and put it on ice.

2. Obtain 5 mL of clear or light colored Gatorade in a small cup.

3. Obtain 5 mL of diluted detergent. The detergent is clear or a color similar to the Gatorade. It has been diluted 50% with water.

4. Chew on the inside of your cheek gently to loosen cells. Take the Gatorade into your mouth but do not swallow it. Swish it around in your mouth for about 30 seconds. Try not to generate too much saliva. After 30 seconds, spit the Gatorade back into the cup.

5. Add 5 mL of detergent and mix gently for two minutes. Try not to generate bubbles.

6. Transfer the Gatorade and detergent to the test tube without generating bubbles.

7. Add several mL of cold ethanol by tilting the tube and pouring the ethanol down the side. The ethanol should form a layer on top of the Gatorade/detergent and not mix.

8. DNA should precipitate at the Gatorade/ethanol interface. It will look cloudy and whitish.

9. Use a transfer pipette to transfer some of the DNA to a microcentrifuge tube. More ethanol needs to be added.

Biology 101 Laboratory Manual

LABORATORY 7 REVIEW
BIOTECHNOLOGY

QUESTIONS

1. What is biotechnology?

   _____

   _____

2. What is the structure of DNA? Draw an illustration if needed.

   _____

   _____

3. Name the four bases in DNA.

   _____

   _____

4. Name the four bases in RNA.

    _____

    _____

5. One strand of DNA has the following sequence: T A C C T C G T A G C G. What is the
    complementary DNA sequence?

    _____

    _____

6. A strand of mRNA has the following sequence: A U G A C C U U U G A G. Use the
    genetic code to determine the protein encoded by the sequence.

    _____

    _____

7. Where is the DNA found in your cheek cells?

    _____

    _____

8. What do you call the group of three bases in RNA that encodes one amino acid in
    the protein?

    _____

    _____

9. What does the Gatorade provide in the isolation of DNA from your cheek cells?

    _____

    _____

10. What is agarose?

    _____

    _____

11. Gel electrophoresis separates molecules bases on _____ and _____.

12. What is the electrical charge of DNA?

_____

_____

13. What is the purpose of the buffer in gel electrophoresis?

_____

_____

14. What is the purpose of the dye markers in electrophoresis?

_____

_____

15. Name the three types of RNA and how they are involved in gene expression.

_____

_____

_____

NOTES

LABORATORY 8
MICROORGANISMS AND DISEASE

LEARNING OBJECTIVES

- Describe the significance of and diverse roles played by microbes.

- Describe basic characteristics of members found from the Domains Bacteria and Archaea.

- Describe major differences between prokaryotes and eukaryotes.

- Prepare and interpret a Gram stain.

- Become familiar with aseptic techniques and procedures used to safely handle bacterial pathogens.

- Identify and isolate bacterial pathogens from biological specimens.

- Interpret standard antimicrobial susceptibility tests.

INTRODUCTION

"Microorganisms account for most of the biomass on the planet and are an essential foundation on which the global ecosystem rests. They play an absolutely essential role in the survival of the human race."

—Carl Woese (Professor of Microbiology, University of Illinois at Urbana-Champaign)

The evolution of cellular organisms is derived from two different lines. Species composed of cells that lack membrane-bound organelles are referred to as **prokaryotes** and typically called bacteria. Cells with membrane-bound organelles are called **eukaryotes** and makeup species of plants, animals, fungi, and protists.

DOMAIN BACTERIA AND ARCHAEA

Research estimates that there may be more than 10 million bacterial species but currently we have identified just 5,000. That means scientists have a long way to go in identifying and describing this diverse group. The characteristics of most bacterial species suggest a very small, single-celled (unicellular) organism that has a rigid cell wall but no true nucleus. The cells may be spherical (coccus), rod-shaped (bacillus), or spiral (spirillum). Due to their small size most prokaryotes were thought to be a unified group of bacteria. Genetic analysis of prokaryotic DNA revealed two very distinct DNA sequences that were both very different from eukaryotes. This led to the development and reorganization of the diversity of life into three domains and five kingdoms. Domain Archaea and Domain Bacteria both are made up of prokaryotes. The most striking difference is that members of the Domain Archaea tend to inhabit but are not restricted to extreme and stressful environments on Earth. Archaea have been thus dubbed the "extremophiles" and most likely are survivors of ancient lines. The kingdom Bacteria are distributed much more widely and in greater numbers than any other group. Scientists utilize microscopes and staining techniques to try and better understand differences between the many and diverse bacterial species.

Table 8.1 Domains and Kingdoms.

Domain	Bacteria	Archaea	Eukarya			
Kingdom	Bacteria	Archaea	Protista	Fungi	Plantae	Animalia
Example		© Eye of Science/ Science Source	*See credit line below.			
Characteristics	Bacteria are simple unicellular organisms.	Archaea are simple unicellular organisms that often live in extreme environments.	Protists are unicellular and are more complex than bacteria or archaea.	Fungi are unicellular or multicellular and absorb food.	Plants are multicellular and make their own food.	Animals are multicellular and take in their food.

* By Doc. RNDr. Josef Reischig, CSc. (Author's archive) [CC BY-SA 3.0 (http://creativecommons.org/licenses/by-sa/3.0)], via Wikimedia Commons from Wikimedia Commons. https://commons.wikimedia.org/wiki/File%3AForaminifera_(251_02)_Mediterranean_Sea.jpg

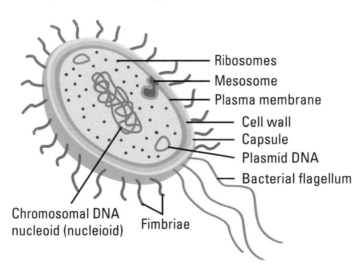

Ribosomes
Mesosome
Plasma membrane
Cell wall
Capsule
Plasmid DNA
Bacterial flagellum
Chromosomal DNA nucleoid (nucleioid)
Fimbriae

Figure 8.1 Generalized Structure of a Prokaryote (bacterial cell).

Table 8.2 The Three Basic Shapes of Bacteria and Typical Arrangements.

Spheres (cocci)		Rods (bacilli)	Spirals
Diplococci (*Streptococcus pneumoniae*)	Streptococci (*Streptococcus pyogenes*)	Chain of bacilli (*Bacillus anthracis*)	Vibrios (*Vibrio cholerae*)
Tetrad	Sarcina (*Sarcina ventriculi*)	Flagellate rods (*Salmonella typhi*)	Spirilla (*Helicobacter pylori*)
Staphylococci (*Staphylococcus aureus*)		Spore-former (*Clostridium botulinum*)	Spirochaetes (*Treponema pallidum*)

It's important to remember that bacteria are found everywhere in soil, water, air, and even us. Most people think of bacteria as causing diseases. While this is true, the majority of bacteria are not pathogenic. Instead, they contribute many beneficial products that make life possible. Their presence directly impacts every aspect of an ecosystem. Consider the following list that highlights a few roles played by microorganisms:

1. Generate oxygen in the atmosphere.

2. Recycle nutrients stored in organic matter to an inorganic form.

3. Fix nitrogen from the atmosphere into a useable form.

4. Allow herbivores to consume poor quality food.

5. Give plant roots access to nutrients in the soil.

6. Microbes protect and boost the immune system.

The following lab procedures will familiarize you with the science and techniques used to identify different types of bacteria. Every student will have the opportunity to look at prepared slides of known cells representing the basic forms of bacteria. Remember, they are **small** and may take a few minutes to find using the microscope. The cells will range in size, shape, and Gram reaction. Each student will receive a live unknown bacterial culture and perform a Gram stain.

THE GRAM STAIN

The most frequently used stain in a clinical microbiology laboratory is the Gram stain. The Gram stain is the first step in trying to identify any unknown bacteria. The stain works by detecting differences in cell wall structure and chemical composition. Bacteria are categorized as either gram-positive (stains dark purple) or gram-negative (stains pink). Gram-positive bacteria are noted for having a thick cell wall, whereas gram-negative bacteria have a much thinner cell wall. In addition to learning the Gram reaction, staining allows the morphology and configuration of the bacteria to be observed (i.e., gram-positive coccus in chains or gram-negative rod) due to increased contrast. Your instructor will go over the Gram stain procedure in detail.

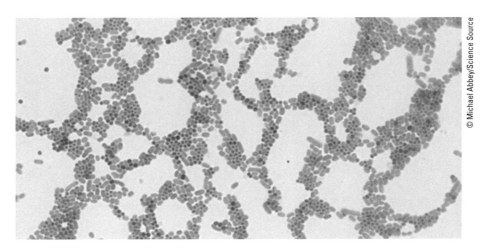

© Michael Abbey/Science Source

Figure 8.2 Gram-Negative. Brightfield Gram stain of *Escherichia coli* and *Staphylococcus aureus* using safranin. The rod-shaped *E. coli* are gram-negative and appear pink. Magnification 400×.

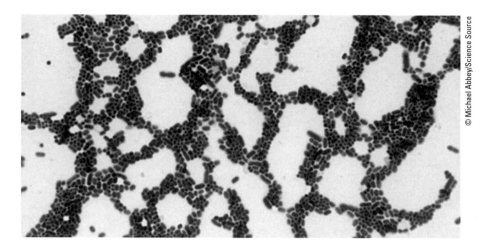

Figure 8.3 Gram-Positive. Brightfield Gram stain of *Escherichia coli* and *Staphylococcus aureus* using iodine. The rod-shaped *E. coli* is gram-negative and appears in a lighter shade of purple, while the *S.aureus* is a gram-positive coccus and appears darker. Magnification 400×.

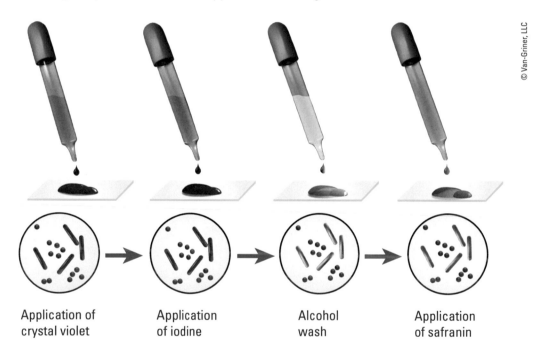

Application of crystal violet

Application of iodine

Alcohol wash

Application of safranin

Figure 8.4 Gram Staining Procedure.

ANTIMICROBIAL SUSCEPTIBILITY

The Gram stain is considered a differential stain because similar looking cells can be placed into two different categories based on color results. This is important information to the medical community that must choose quickly the correct treatment to fight infections caused by bacteria. Antibiotics work in a variety of ways to kill bacteria (i.e., inhibit cell wall or protein synthesis). Bacteria respond very differently to the wide range of antibiotics. The response can be categorized as very sensitive, slightly sensitive (intermediate), or even resistant to particular antibiotics. Standard methods have been developed and used to measure susceptibility of bacterial isolates to antibiotics. The Kirby-Bauer Method, or disk diffusion method, is the most commonly used and convenient approach. Special paper disks containing specific amounts of antibiotics are placed on a lawn of bacteria inoculated on a solid agar medium. The antibiotics begin to diffuse radially through the agar. Depending upon the reaction (sensitivity) of the bacterium to the antibiotic a clear zone (zone of inhibition) without growth appears around each disk. The diameter of each zone can be measured in millimeters and compared to a standard reference table to determine sensitivity.

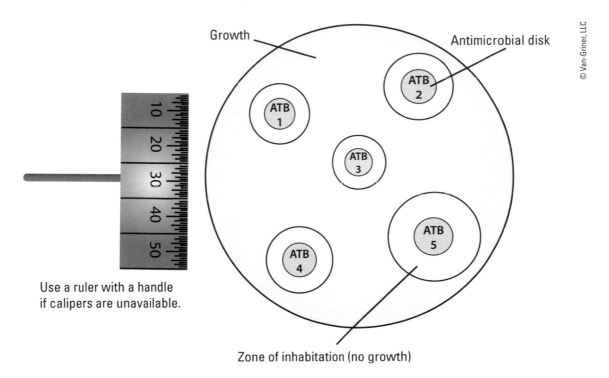

Figure 8.5 How to Interpret Sensitivity Plate Results.

LAB ACTIVITIES

GRAM STAIN—PREPARED SLIDES OF KNOWN BACTERIA

1. Obtain prepared slides of stained bacteria. These slides contain different gram-positive and gram-negative bacteria.

2. Practice looking and determining the Gram stain reaction as well as basic shape and/or arrangement of bacteria.

3. Sketch and record what you see.

GRAM STAIN—LIVE KNOWN AND UNKNOWN BACTERIAL CULTURES ISOLATED FROM BIOLOGICAL SPECIMENS

1. Obtain a clean slide, label, wax pencil, Bunsen burner, bibulous paper, and an inoculating loop.

2. Working with a lab partner, carefully pick up a tray of biological stains and test tube rack containing live bacterial cultures.

3. Record and label the slide. Use the wax pencil to draw a circle in the middle of the slide.

4. Using a sterile inoculating loop transfer one liquid drop to a clean slide and spread it evenly out. Your instructor will demonstrate proper aseptic technique. It is important to use sterile techniques when opening, sampling, and closing a culture tube of bacteria to prevent contamination to the culture and handler!

5. Allow the liquid on the slide to air dry.

6. Once dry, the sample must be heat fixed onto the slide. Gently hold the slide with a clothespin and pass it over the top of the Bunsen burner flame twice. Be careful to avoid heating the slide too much or too little.

7. Let the slide cool.

8. Place the cooled slide onto the staining rack over the sink. Drench the bacterial smear with the primary dye, crystal violet, for one minute.

9. Rinse the slide with water until the excess stain is removed (about five seconds). Shake excess water off. It is not necessary to blot dry.

10. Place the slide back onto the staining rack. Flood the smear with Gram's iodine for one minute.

11. Rinse the slide with water and remove excess stain. Shake excess water off. Again, there is no need to dry the slide.

> **CAUTION** This next step (decolorization) takes practice and needs your undivided attention. How much time to decolorize depends on multiple factors such as smear thickness and alcohol concentration.

12. Hold the slide at a 45-degree angle and apply the decolorizer slowly one drop at a time over the smear. Make sure the drops run equally over and down the surface of the smear. When there is no longer a purple tinge to the drops stop and immediately rinse the smear.

13. Shake excess water off and do not blot dry.

14. Flood the smear with the counterstain, safranin, for one minute.

15. Rinse excess safranin from the slide (about five seconds).

16. Blot dry using bibulous paper.

17. Repeat procedure for remaining cultures.

18. Observe the stained slides and determine the Gram reaction.

19. Sketch and record results.

Table 8.3 Results from Gram Stain Procedure.

Microorganism	Form	Gram Reaction

KIRBY-BAUER ANTIBIOTIC SENSITIVITY TESTING

1. Obtain several Kirby-Bauer plates prepared ahead of time by your instructor. The plates represent different cultures of gram-positive and gram-negative bacteria exposed to common antibiotics.

2. With your lab partner, measure and record any zones of inhibition.

3. Refer to the standard reference table passed out during class.

4. Determine the sensitivity reaction for each of your measurements.

5. Based on your Gram reaction earlier, which of the antibiotics would you prescribe to treat an infection caused by your unknown?

Table 8.4 Antimicrobial Sensitivity Results.

Antibiotic	Plate 1	Plate 2	Plate 3

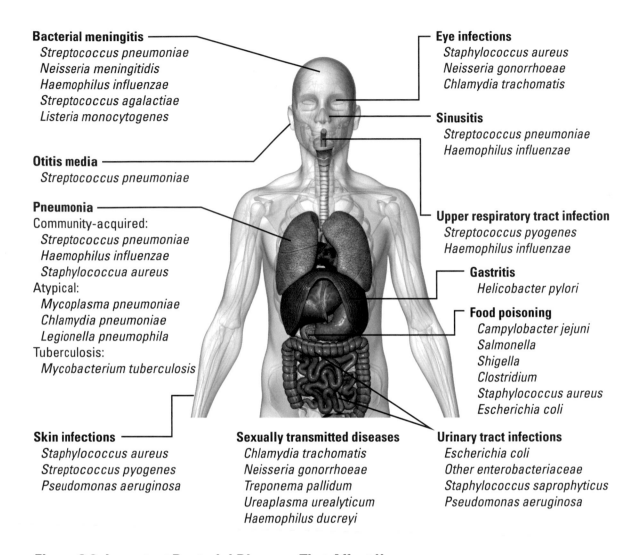

Bacterial meningitis
Streptococcus pneumoniae
Neisseria meningitidis
Haemophilus influenzae
Streptococcus agalactiae
Listeria monocytogenes

Otitis media
Streptococcus pneumoniae

Pneumonia
Community-acquired:
Streptococcus pneumoniae
Haemophilus influenzae
Staphylococcua aureus
Atypical:
Mycoplasma pneumoniae
Chlamydia pneumoniae
Legionella pneumophila
Tuberculosis:
Mycobacterium tuberculosis

Skin infections
Staphylococcus aureus
Streptococcus pyogenes
Pseudomonas aeruginosa

Sexually transmitted diseases
Chlamydia trachomatis
Neisseria gonorrhoeae
Treponema pallidum
Ureaplasma urealyticum
Haemophilus ducreyi

Eye infections
Staphylococcus aureus
Neisseria gonorrhoeae
Chlamydia trachomatis

Sinusitis
Streptococcus pneumoniae
Haemophilus influenzae

Upper respiratory tract infection
Streptococcus pyogenes
Haemophilus influenzae

Gastritis
Helicobacter pylori

Food poisoning
Campylobacter jejuni
Salmonella
Shigella
Clostridium
Staphylococcus aureus
Escherichia coli

Urinary tract infections
Escherichia coli
Other enterobacteriaceae
Staphylococcus saprophyticus
Pseudomonas aeruginosa

Figure 8.6 Important Bacterial Diseases That Affect Humans.

Biology 101 Laboratory Manual

LABORATORY 8 REVIEW
MICROORGANISMS AND DISEASE

QUESTIONS

1. Why are bacteria classified as prokaryotes?

2. What makes prokaryotic organisms different than eukaryotic organisms?

3. How are members of the Domain Archaea different from Domain Bacteria?

4. What are the three basic shapes of bacteria and what do they look like?

_____

_____

5. What are some typical arrangements of bacteria?

_____

_____

6. What is aseptic technique? How do you perform it?

_____

_____

7. What are two ecological roles performed by microorganisms?

_____

_____

8. Explain why the Gram stain is considered such an important diagnostic tool.

_____

_____

9. Explain why gram-positive bacteria appear purple/blue whereas gram-negative bacteria appear red after performing a Gram stain?

_____

_____

10. What are the primary dye, mordant, and counterstain used in the Gram stain?

_____

_____

NAME:_____ DATE:_____

11. Why is it important to have a thin smear of bacteria on the slide?

_____

_____

12. Why is heat fixing important before staining a bacterial smear?

_____

_____

13. What is the purpose of performing a Kirby-Bauer Disk Diffusion Susceptibility Test?

_____

_____

14. What is a "zone of inhibition?"

_____

_____

15. Discuss one of the bacterial diseases that affect humans from Figure 8.6. What are the causes, symptoms, etc.?

_____

_____

NOTES

LABORATORY 9
PROTISTS AND FUNGI

LEARNING OBJECTIVES

- Identify organisms found in the Kingdom Protista.

- Observe basic characteristics of protozoans, algae, and slime molds.

- Observe basic characteristics of Kingdom Fungi.

- Describe the basic anatomy of a typical mushroom.

- Identify the three main forms of lichens.

INTRODUCTION

KINGDOM PROTISTA—PROTOZOANS, SLIME MOLDS, AND ALGAE

Kingdom Protista is a diverse group of eukaryotic organisms. The diversity within Protista is relatively unknown due to the sheer number of species that belong to this Kingdom, with estimates ranging from 40,000 to upwards of 200,000 or more species. With this amount of diversity, both heterotrophic and autotrophic organisms have been found and identified. If a protist is heterotrophic, the organism cannot produce its own food, but rather relies on other sources, whereas an autotrophic protist can synthesize their own food. Within Protista, there are three main groups: protozoans, slime molds, and algae.

PROTOZOANS

Protozoans are mostly unicellular heterotrophic organisms that will ingest food by forming food vacuoles. Food vacuoles are membrane bound sacs with digestive functions. In the protozoans, most are **heterotrophic** but some species can be **autotrophic.** Such a protozoan is *Euglena* (Figure 9.3). *Euglena* species can be found in both fresh and salt water and contain chloroplasts, but can also consume food by phagocytosis. Phagocytosis is the process of surrounding and engulfing food particles. Therefore, *Euglena* species will utilize phagocytosis and photosynthesis, allowing it to obtain nutrients by different methods, a lifestyle that is termed mixotrophic. In addition to a varied means of obtaining nutrients, each group of protozoa generally has a unique mode of locomotion. For example, paramecia use **cilia** (short hair-like structures) (Figure 9.1), amoebas use **pseudopodia** (temporary extensions of the cell) (Figure 9.2), and *Euglena* use **flagella** (long tail-like structures) as their primary forms of movement (Figure 9.3).

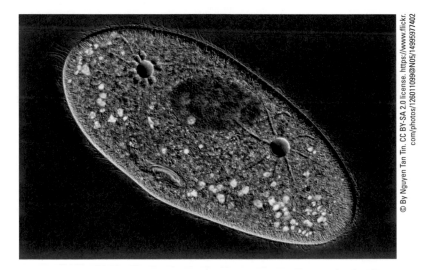

Figure 9.1 *Paramecium* **with Cilia.** Light micrograph showing a *Paramecium,* a single-celled organism. *Paramecium* showing macronucleus, water expulsion vacuolas and mounth. Magnification 20×.

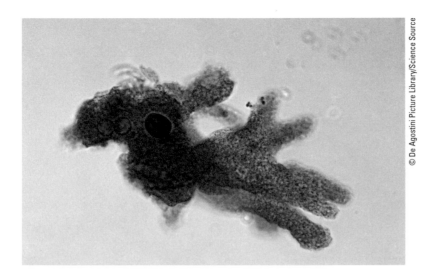

Figure 9.2 Amoeba with Pseudopodia. Light micrograph (LM) of amoeba (*Amoeba proteus*), Protozoan, seen with counterstaining. Magnification 160× at 35 mm.

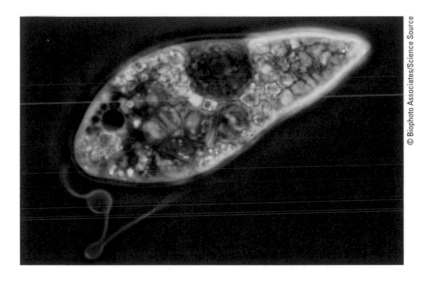

Figure 9.3 *Euglena* with Flagella. Light micrograph of *Euglena* sp., living cell showing locomotory flagellum, eyespot (red), chloroplasts (green), contractile vacuole (sphere near eyespot), small accessory vacuoles, central nucleus with chromosomes, and paramylon (in cell posterior). Anoptral contrast. Magnification 500× at 35 mm.

Just as locomotion is varied in protists, so is the means of reproduction, with many protozoa exhibiting more than one strategy. **Binary fission,** dividing a cell into two equal and identical cells, is the asexual reproduction in a *Paramecium* (Figure 9.4). However, *Paramecium* can also reproduce by conjugation. **Conjugation** is when genetic material is transferred between two cells via a conjugation tube (Figure 9.5). Other types of protozoa can reproduce by **budding,** a process of a new individual arising by growths from an existing organism. *Vorticella,* a stalked, inverted bell shaped ciliate that lives in fresh water ponds and streams utilize budding (Figure 9.6).

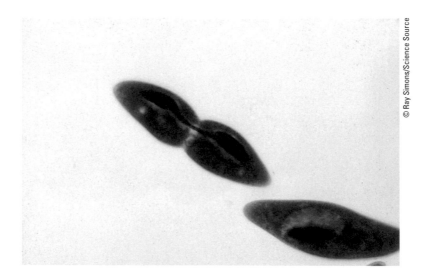

Figure 9.4 Binary Fission. Binary fission, or mitosis of a *Paramecium.*

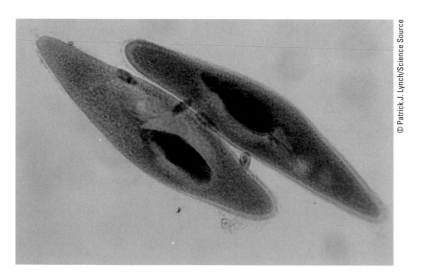

Figure 9.5 Conjugation. Light micrograph (LM) showing *Paramecium* micronucleatum during conjugation (a form of sexual reproduction in which micronuclei are exchanged). Magnification 200× at 35 mm.

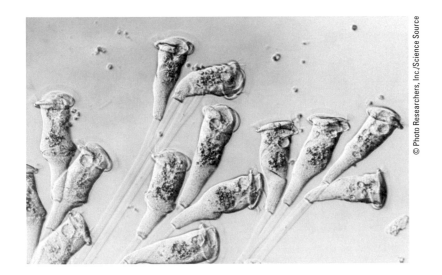

Figure 9.6 Budding. Color enhanced light micrograph of *Vorticella,* a stalked, inverted, bell-shaped ciliate that inhabits freshwater ponds and streams; in oblique light. Magnification unknown.

With the diversity of this group, protozoa sometimes are harmful to humans. Some can cause diseases like sleeping sickness. *Trypanosoma* is a flagellated protozoan that causes sleeping sickness in humans (Figure 9.7). This sleeping sickness is a neurological disease that is fatal if not treated. Many have also been found to pollute drinking water and/or be parasitic.

Figure 9.7 *Trypanosoma* Infection Causing Sleeping Sickness. *Trypanosoma brucei* on red blood cells. The parasites which cause African sleeping sickness are transmitted to humans by the tsetse fly. Computer generated image.

SLIME MOLDS

The next main group of protists are the slime molds. Slime molds are a group that are **saprotrophic,** meaning they obtain food from dead and decaying organisms. This group will also form characteristic spores at some point within their life cycle. There are two types of slime molds, plasmodial and cellular. Plasmodial slime molds exist as a fan shaped, multi-nucleated mass of cytoplasm (plasmodium) while cellular slime molds exist as individual amoeboid cells, which aggregate occasionally to form a pseudoplasmodium.

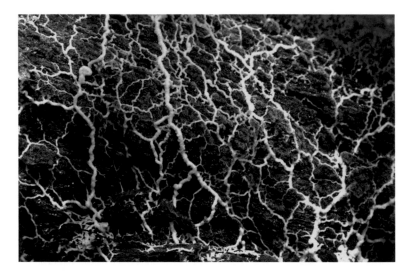

Figure 9.8 Slime Mold. Plasmodium of slime mold (myxomycete) spreading over a moist log.

Figure 9.9 Slime Mold. Slime mold (*Hemitrichia calyculata*) growing on dead wood, Clumber Park, Nottinghamshire, England.

ALGAE

The third main group found in Protista are the algae. Algae are a mostly aquatic, photosynthetic group of organisms that are not plants. They do not have structures found with most nonvascular and vascular plants like rhizoids, roots, or leaves and they do not protect the zygote and other reproductive structures like plants do. What they do have in common with plants is that they are primary producers that release oxygen from the process of photosynthesis. There are various types of algae, some of which are green algae, red algae, and yellow-brown algae.

Spirogyra is a type of green algae that is filamentous and has a characteristic ribbon like chloroplast (Figure 9.10). *Spirogyra* also exhibits conjugation which occurs between two filaments, moving the contents from one organism to another. *Volvox* is another green algae, but this green algae is a **colony** (Figure 9.11). Thousands of cells make up one colony and each have flagella, thus they are capable of locomotion. *Volvox* also exhibits both asexual and sexual reproduction. In asexual reproduction, the colony can divide to produce **daughter colonies** (Figure 9.12). During sexual reproduction some colonies produce sperm and some produce eggs. The yellow-brown algae contain diatoms. Diatoms are widespread around oceans, freshwater, and soil (Figure 9.13). They are unique in that they have silica in their cell walls instead of cellulose like most plants. This silica does not decompose and is therefore very abundant, this diatomaceous Earth is then mined and used in various ways such as in filters and as insecticides.

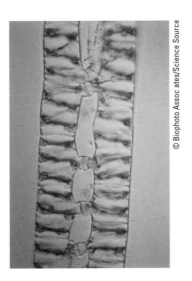

Figure 9.10 *Spirogyra* Exhibiting Conjugation Tubes. Light micrograph of *Spirogyra*, a filamentous green algae, preparing for reproduction.

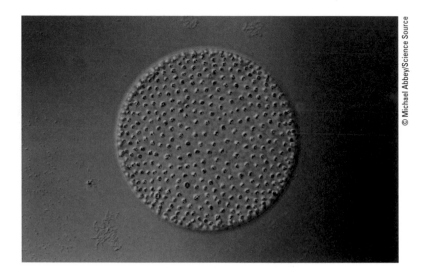

Figure 9.11 *Volvox* Colony. Light micrograph (LM) of the green algae species *Volvox globator* (living). Magnification 75× at 35 mm.

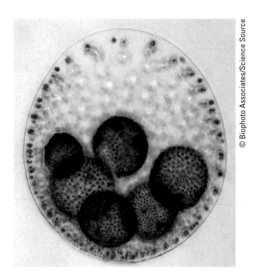

Figure 9.12 *Volvox* Daughter Cells. Color enhanced light micrograph of coenobium of *Volvox tertius,* with six daughter coenobia ready for release. Living, magnified 200× at 4″ × 4″.

Figure 9.13 Diatoms. Light micrograph of a variety of centric diatoms. Magnification unknown.

KINGDOM FUNGI

Fungi are a group of organisms that are **saprotrophic.** Fungi have cell walls like plants, but unlike plants the cell walls are made of chitin instead of cellulose. The fungal body consists of strands called **hyphae** which collectively are called a **mycellum,** when many of these strands come together they form a fungal body. Within the hyphae, **septa** (walls) can be seen separating the nuclei and spores may be produced from the tips of hyphae. **Spores** are small haploid structures with a protective covering. These spores are used for both sexual and asexual reproduction.

RHIZOPUS

Rhizopus species are common saprotrophic fungi. This type of fungi can be easily found by leaving baked goods uncovered, such as bread (Figure 9.14). *Rhizopus* species are filamentous branching hyphae that exhibit both sexual and asexual reproduction. From the hyphae, a **sporgangium** (enclosure where spores form) will develop on a stalk-like structure (Figure 9.15). The spores formed here are used in asexual reproduction, allowing the spores to spread and germinate. For sexual reproduction, a zygospore will be created by differing ends of hyphae (Figure 9.16). This **zygospore** is a diploid ($2n$) reproductive structure that once it undergoes meiosis will create haploid (n) spores for germination.

Figure 9.14 Bread Mold.

Figure 9.15 Sporgangium. Bread mold fungus (*Rhizopus nigricans*) growing on bread left in a moist plastic bag for seven days. Tangled mycelium (vegetative filaments) are visible as well as sporangia bearing spores. 3:1 magnification. Dallas, Texas.

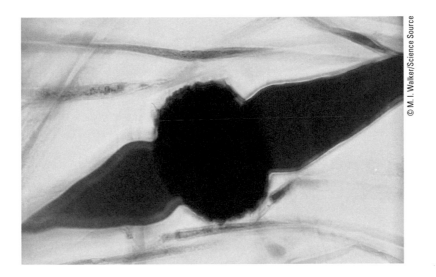

Figure 9.16 Zygospore. Light micrograph of *Rhizopus* sp. zygospore; phase contrast. Magnification 100× at 35 mm.

CLUB FUNGI

The fungi that most people are familiar with are the club fungi. Club fungi are a group that includes mushrooms (Figure 9.17 and Figure 9.18). The actual body of the mushroom is the spore producing fruiting body that is called a **basidiocarp,** and some exhibit a **pileus** (cap). A basidiocarp will come about from the joining of + and − hyphae. **Gills** are found on the underside of the cap, and these are the sites of spore production in these fungi. Spores are referred to as **basidiospores,** and are created from fusing nuclei of **basidia** and then undergoing meiosis.

Figure 9.17 Mushroom Anatomy. 1. Stalk, 2. Gills, 3. Annulus, 4. Pileus (cap).

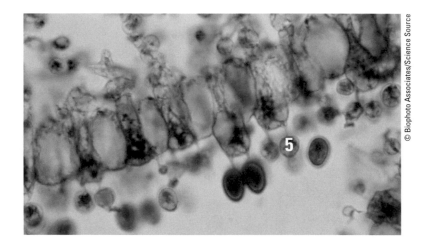

Figure 9.18 Mushroom Anatomy. 5. Basidiospore. *Agaricus bisporus* is a commercial mushroom. Section of gill showing two basidiospores on each basidium, instead of the four found on the wild-type. This is a type of Basidiomycete, which is characterized by basidia, club-shaped structures borne on gills, pores or other fertile surfaces. Each basidium typically buds off four basidiospores after a sexual process and meiosis. The spores germinate to produce a mycelium (often underground, in leaf litter, inside trees, etc.) from which arise the fruit bodies (mushrooms, toadstools, etc.).

LICHENS

Also found in Kingdom Fungi are lichens. Lichens are a fungus that **symbiotically** (long-term association between organisms) lives with an alga or cyanobacteria. The fungi present is generally an ascomycete. Lichens come in many sizes, colors, and forms. The three most common forms are **crustose** (encrusting), **foliose** (leaf like), and **fruticose** (shrub like) (Figure 9.19). These forms may look similar to plants but they are not. Lichens do not have roots like plants or mosses that will absorb water or nutrients. They grow on surfaces of rocks, trees, and rotting logs as a substrate to grow on only. Lichens will produce their own food from the photosynthetic portion and the fungal portion which will help protect them from the environment.

Figure 9.19 Lichens on a Dead Branch.

LAB ACTIVITIES

PROTOZOAN

LOCOMOTION

1. Obtain a live sample of each protozoan (*Euglena, Amoeba, Paramecium*) and make a wet mount slide. If needed, a protist slowing solution can be used to slow the movements of the organisms.

2. Observe the means of locomotion for each organism.

3. Draw each organism, noting structures such as cilia, pseudopodia, and flagella.

REPRODUCTION

1. Obtain prepared slides of *Paramecium and Vorticella.*

2. Observe the means of reproduction in each organism (binary fission, conjugation, or budding).

3. Draw each organism and label each strategy of reproduction and various structures.

DISEASE

1. Obtain a prepared slide of *Trypanosoma.*

2. Observe and draw the trypanosome.

SLIME MOLDS

1. Observe and draw a plasmodial slime mold under a dissecting microscope.

ALGAE

1. Obtain either live samples or prepared slides of *Spirogyra, Volvox,* and diatoms. (Other algae may be viewed depending on availability.)

   a. Observe and draw each sample: Identify unique structures (i.e., conjugation tubes, daughter colony ....)

2. Obtain a sample of pond water.

   a. Create a wet mount slide.

   b. Observe and classify all organisms found in pond water as either protozoan, algae, or diatom.

FUNGI

RHIZOPUS

1. Observe a common bread mold. (Do not take bread out of bag.)

2. Obtain a prepared slide of *Rhizopus* sporangium.

   a. Draw sporangium and identify zygospores.

CLUB FUNGI

1. Obtain a typical mushroom from your instructor.

   a. Identify structures of the mushroom as indicated by your instructor.

   b. Dissect the basidiocarp and view gills under a dissecting microscope and/or compound microscope to observe spores.

2. Obtain a prepared slide of basidia to view basidiospores and draw.

LICHENS

1. Obtain various samples of Lichens.

   a. Identify each sample as crustose, foliose, or fruticose.

Biology 101 Laboratory Manual

LABORATORY 9 REVIEW
PROTISTS AND FUNGI

QUESTIONS

1. In your observations of the amoeba, live or preserved, what did you observe about how they move?

_____

_____

2. What is a pseudopod?

_____

_____

3. What are the ways protozoans obtain food?

_____

_____

4. What is a contractile vacuole? Give an example of an organism that uses a contractile vacuole.

_____

_____

5. What role do algae and fungi play in ecosystems?

_____

_____

6. It is sometimes said that diatoms live in glass houses. Explain.

_____

_____

7. What type of nutrition do algae have?

_____

_____

8. Explain the different ways that protozoa are able to move? Give an example of an organism that uses each.

_____

_____

9. What is a slime mold? Explain the different types.

_____

_____

_____

10. What is the site of spore production in club fungi?

_____

_____

_____

NAME:_____ DATE:_____

11. What do fungi produce during both sexual and asexual reproduction?

_____

_____

_____

12. What is conjugation and which organisms discussed use it?

_____

_____

_____

13. How does *Volvox* reproduce?

_____

_____

_____

14. What characteristics do organisms in the Kingdom Protista exhibit?

_____

_____

_____

15. What characteristics do organisms in the Kingdom Fungi exhibit?

_____

_____

_____

NOTES

LABORATORY 10
A SURVEY OF PLANT DIVERSITY

LEARNING OBJECTIVES

■ Understand the importance of plants.

■ Know the difference between nonvascular and vascular plants.

■ Understand the characteristics of the nonvascular plants, particularly bryophytes and liverworts.

■ Understand the importance of the vascular tissue xylem and phloem and how it allowed plants to increase in size.

■ Identify and understand the basic process of how seedless vascular plants reproduce with spores.

■ Understand the importance of the evolution of the seed.

■ Understand why the gymnosperms are "naked seed" plants and what that means in terms of their reproduction.

- Understand the basic characteristics of angiosperms.

- Understand the importance of the evolution of flowers and fruit and how it has made angiosperms so successful.

- Understand basic anatomy of flowers and fruits.

INTRODUCTION

In this lab you will be doing a survey of the plant kingdom and learning some basic characters of the different groups of plants. Plants are multicellular eukaryotes and photosynthetic autotrophs. One character that separates plants from their green algae ancestors is a distinct alternation of generations between haploid (1n) and diploid (2n) stages. What this means is that in the life cycle of plants there is a distinct haploid stage, called the gametophyte, and a distinct diploid stage, called the sporophyte. The gametophyte stage produces haploid gametes which, upon fertilization, will form a new sporophyte. The sporophyte stage produces haploid spores, by meiosis, which will grow into new gametophytes.

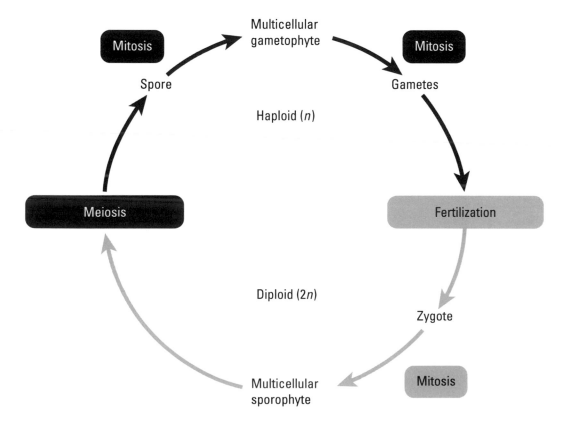

Figure 10.1 Alternation of Generations in Plants.

BRYOPHYTES

The first group of plants we will discuss are the bryophytes, commonly known as mosses and liverworts. These plants are generally quite small in size due to a lack of vascular tissues to transport water and dissolved solutes throughout the plant. Bryophytes have a very distinct alternation of generations with the haploid gametophyte being the dominant organisms in the life cycle. In fact, the diploid sporophyte remains attached to the gametophyte and dependent upon it for nutrition (see Figure 10.2, Figure 10.3, and Figure 10.4).

Figure 10.2 Moss Sporophytes with Spore Capsules. On this moss you can see the green gametophyte plants at the bottom and the sporophytes growing as stalks with capsules growing out of the gametophytes.

Figure 10.3 Gametophyte of the Liverwort *Marchantia*. Thallose liverworts, a division of non-vascular bryophyte land plants commonly referred to as hepatophytes or liverworts.

Figure 10.4 Sporophytes of the Liverwort *Marchantia*. Liverwort (*Marchantia polymorpha*).

SEEDLESS VASCULAR PLANTS

The next group of plants to discuss are the seedless vascular plants, the most familiar of which are the ferns. Although the group also contains plants called horsetails, whisk ferns, and club mosses, we will focus on the ferns. The first major difference between the bryophytes and the seedless vascular plants is the presence of vascular tissue, particularly xylem and phloem. Xylem is the tissue that transports water and minerals whereas phloem transports sugars made by photosynthesis and other molecules throughout the plant. Because of this ability to transport materials throughout the plant body, these plants are able to be larger in size. A second major difference here is that the sporophyte has become the dominant life stage, and the gametophyte is greatly reduced in size to a small gamete producing plant.

Figure 10.5 Ostrich Ferns, *Matteuccia struthiopteris*.

Figure 10.6 Holly Fern Frond. Notice the sori which are where the spores are produced.

Figure 10.7 Fern Gametophyte. These are typically about the size of a fingernail.

SEED PLANTS

The next group of plants to talk about is the seed plants, which consist of the gymnosperms and angiosperms. We will consider the gymnosperms first. The term gymnosperm means "naked seed" because the seeds are produced directly on the surface of some reproductive structures. The gymnosperms with which people are most familiar are the conifers, or cone bearing trees such as pines, and this is the group that will be focused on in this lab. Because of the presence of vascular tissue, these plants are able to get quite large in size, as evidenced by the giant redwoods *Sequoiadendron giganteum* of California. (See Figure 10.8.)

Figure 10.8 A Giant Sequoia, *Sequoiadendron giganteum.* Mariposa Grove, Yosemite National Park, California.

The reproduction in conifers involves cones, and these cones are of two types, male and female. The male, or pollen, cones are usually found on the end of the tree's branches so that they are exposed to the wind, which will transport the pollen. It is inside of these cones where meiosis occurs, resulting in the immature male gametophyte, which is a pollen grain. (See Figure 10.9.) Depending on the species, female, or ovulate seed, cone development and maturation takes two to three years. (See Figure 10.10.) It is in the female cones that meiosis also occurs, producing four products, only one of which will form a mature multicellular female gametophyte containing eggs located near the opening of the ovules. Once a pollen grain is deposited onto a female cone near the ovule it germinates and one of its cells begins growing a pollen tube toward the ovule. Another of the pollen grain cells divides and forms two sperm cells which will travel down the pollen tube. One sperm will fuse with the egg, the other will degenerate. After fertilization a zygote will form and eventually a mature seed.

© Max Pixel. CC0 1.0 license. http://maxpixel.freegreatpicture.com/Conifer-Scots-Pine-Evergreen-Pinus-Pollen-1211170

Figure 10.9 Male Pine Cones Giving off Pollen. The male cone is releasing a cloud of pollen.

Figure 10.10 Female Pine Cones, or Ovulate Seed Cones.

Angiosperms, which are the flowering plants, are the most familiar to most people. The term Angiosperm translates as "vessel seed" and refers to the female portion of the plant called the carpel, which is where the ovules are found. The major character that identifies a seed plant as an angiosperm is the presence of a flower structure, parts of which will mature into a fruit. (See Figure 10.11.) Currently close to 300,000 species of angiosperms have been identified, and, just as in the seedless vascular plants and gymnosperms, the sporophyte is the dominant life stage, while the gametophyte is reduced to just a small number of gamete producing cells which are completely dependent on the sporophyte.

Reproductively, when a pollen grain lands on the stigma of the flower, it germinates, meaning that one cell forms a pollen tube and another cell undergoes mitosis and forms two sperm which will travel down the pollen tube towards the ovule(s) found inside the ovary. Upon this pollen germination, the mature male gametophyte has been formed. The female gametophyte is found inside each ovule, and it also consists of only a few cells. Once the pollen tube enters the female gametophyte one sperm fertilizes the haploid egg nucleus forming a diploid zygote, and the other sperm fuses with two polar nuclei in the female gametophyte to form a triploid ($3n$) endosperm which will provide nutrition for the sporophyte embryo as it develops within the seed. (See Figure 10.12.)

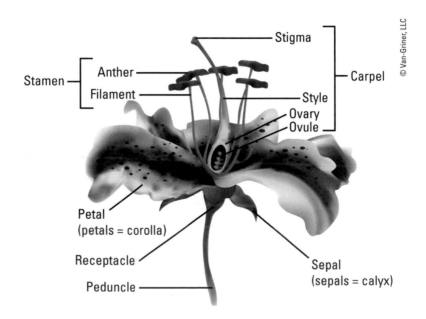

© Van-Griner, LLC

Figure 10.11 **Structure of a Typical Flower.**

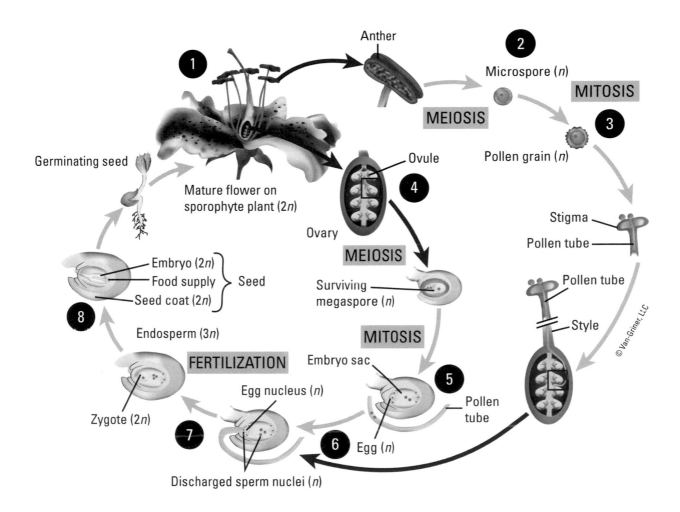

Figure 10.12 Life Cycle of a Typical Angiosperm.

LAB ACTIVITIES

NON VASCULAR PLANTS

1. Obtain a sample of the liverwort *Marchantia* gametophyte.

2. Under the dissecting scope examine the specimen, and look for the structures called gemmae cups. These are where structures called gemmae are found which will detach and splash out to land somewhere else and grow into new individuals.

3. Obtain a specimen of the common moss, *Sphagnum.* This is the moss commonly sold in garden centers and harvested as peat moss for use in horticulture.

4. Examine the moss under the dissecting scope, paying attention to the structures.

SEEDLESS VASCULAR PLANTS

1. Obtain a specimen of the common horsetail, *Equisetum.*

2. Locate the nodes in the stem. This is where some species produce small scale like leaves.

3. Locate the strobilus at the top of the plant and examine it under the dissecting scope. This is where the spores are produced that, if they land in a suitable location, will produce the gametophyte generation.

4. Obtain a specimen of a common fern sporophyte.

5. Under the dissecting scope observe a fern frond and locate the sori. These are where spores are produced that will grow into a small, heart shaped fern gametophyte.

SEED PLANTS

GYMNOSPERMS

1. Obtain samples of typical conifer cones. There are two types, the most familiar ovulate seed, or female, cones, and the smaller pollen, or male, cone. Also, obtain a sample of a typical conifer seed.

2. Observe the female cones and identify the spots on each scale where the seeds developed and are shed.

3. Observe the pollen cones and the seeds under the dissecting scope. Notice that the seed is not enclosed in a fruit, which is why these are the naked seed plants.

ANGIOSPERMS

1. Obtain a sample of a typical flower.

2. Locate the parts of the flower, as shown in Figure 10.11, and using a scalpel slice through the ovary. Observe this under the dissecting scope and locate the ovules located within.

3. Observe the various samples of different fruits provided in the lab.

4. Using a handout or display provided in the lab, slice into the fruits, observe the internal structures, and identify the different types of fruits. For example, are they berries, drupes, aggregate fruits, etc.?

Aggregate Fruits. Developed from single flower that has multiple carpels and pistils, which form fruitlets.			
RASPBERRY		BLACKBERRY	
STRAWBERRIES	Formed by the receptacle of the flower instead of the carpels and pistils. The seeds of the strawberry are actually achene dry fruits.		

Composite or Multiple Fruits. One fruit developed by many flowers.					
PINEAPPLE		FIG		MULBERRY	

Simple Fruits. Developed from one single flower with one carpel and one pistil. Can be dry and fleshy.					
LEGUME	Peas	Peanuts	**PEPO**	Watermelon	Pumpkin
NUT	Hazelnut	Acorn	**DRUPE**	Peach	Cherry
SAMARA	Maple		**FIBROUS DRUPE**	Coconut	
BERRY	Tomato	Kiwi	**POME**	Apple	Pear
BERRY	Blueberries	Peppers	**HESPERIDIUM**	Lemon	Orange
BERRY	Cucumber	Banana	**ACHENE**	Sunflower	Dandelion

Biology 101 Laboratory Manual

LABORATORY 10 REVIEW
A SURVEY OF PLANT DIVERSITY

FIELD GUIDE—15 POINTS

For this part of the lab you will prepare a small "field guide" of the specimens you have observed in lab. This will include drawings of each specimen with structures that you were to identify labeled accordingly.

QUESTIONS—15 POINTS

1. What is the difference between a sporophyte and a gametophyte?

    _____

    _____

    _____

2. What is the major character that separates the bryophytes from the other groups of plants you observed?

   _____

   _____

3. What is vascular tissue in plants? Give two examples.

   _____

   _____

4. In the evolution of plants, what was the advantage of the development of vascular tissue?

   _____

   _____

5. What are the major differences between the bryophytes and seedless vascular plants?

   _____

   _____

6. Why are spores so important in the reproduction of the seedless vascular plants, such as ferns?

   _____

   _____

7. Why are gymnosperms, such as the conifers, called naked seed plants?

   _____

   _____

8. Describe the differences between male and female cones in gymnosperms.

   _____

   _____

NAME: _____ DATE: _____

9. Why have flowers allowed angiosperms to become so successful as a group?

_____

_____

10. What are the female parts of the flower? Explain each.

_____

_____

11. What are the male parts of the flower? Explain each.

_____

_____

12. What is a drupe? Give an example.

_____

_____

13. What is a pome? Give an example.

_____

_____

14. What are two of the types of fruits you observed in lab, and how did you identify them?

_____

_____

15. What type of fruit is a legume? Explain.

_____

_____

NOTES

LABORATORY 11
ANIMAL DIVERSITY, PART 1

SURVEY OF THE ANIMAL KINGDOM—PHYLA PORIFERA, CNIDARIA, PLATYHELMINTHES, MOLLUSCA, AND NEMATODA

LEARNING OBJECTIVES

■ Understand how organisms survive and succeed in their environment with specific structures and adaptations.

■ Identify characteristics of the phyla and the characteristics of some of the classes that are in each.

■ Differentiate body forms and general life cycles of selected organisms in each phylum.

■ Recognize specific structures from selected organisms in each phylum.

INTRODUCTION

ANIMAL KINGDOM

Animals are among the most abundant and diverse living organisms. They can be found in almost every habitat on Earth and many species have yet to be discovered. Despite their diversity and wide range of habitats animals all share these distinct characteristics in common.

1. Animals have their own mode of locomotion at some point in their lifecycle.

2. Animals are multi-cellular.

3. Animal cells do not have cell walls like plants do.

4. Animals are heterotrophic. Animals obtain their energy from other sources because they cannot produce their own food.

Organisms that share these characteristics are found in the Kingdom Animalia. In lab, we will be studying several of the phyla that make up the Kingdom Animalia. These phyla are Porifera, Cnidaria, Platyhelminthes, Mollusca, Nematoda, Arthropoda, Echinodermata, and Chordata.

LAB ACTIVITIES

PHYLUM PORIFERA

Phylum Porifera are most commonly known as the sponges. These animals consist of species that mostly live in salt water environments. Sponges have a loose body organization of tissue and most lack symmetry. Adult sponges are sessile, however, larval forms of sponges are free-swimming. Sponges lack both a mouth and an anus. Sponges obtain food by filtering seawater and removing food particles from it.

Cells of sponges are organized on the outside of their bodies with flat epithelial cells. The insides of sponges have a central cavity lined by flagellated cells called **choanocytes** or collar cells. These cells push water through the sponge where food is trapped. Filtered water then exits a hole found in the end of a sponge called an **osculum.**

Between the outer epithelial cells and inner layers of choanocyte cells, sponges also contain needles of calcium carbonate or silica called **spicules** and a protein called **spongin.** Spicules and spongin form a type of skeleton and provide protection for the sponge. Commercial bath sponges (the natural ones) that humans use are composed of the skeleton made of spongin and spicules from a marine sponge.

Sponges can reproduce both sexually and asexually. Through asexual reproduction, sponges can break into fragments naturally, through the environment or through a predator and still survive. New broken fragments of a sponge can make entirely new individual sponges. Sexual reproduction is achieved by transformed choanocytes that produce sperm and release the sperm into the water where, with some luck, it is carried to another sponge of the same species.

Figure 11.1 Natural Commercial Sponge.

Figure 11.2 Operculum of Tube Sponge. Macro showing opening (operculum) at top of stove pipe sponge (*Aplysina archeri*). Turks and Caicos.

OBSERVE STRUCTURES OF THE SPONGES

Examine a preserved sponge specimen, *Scypha.* Cut the sponge in half and see if you can distinguish different structures as shown in the figure below. Structures found in sponges that you should check for are the outside epithelial layer of cells, the spongocoel or the inside cavity in which water passes through and is filtered for food by the choanocytes or collar cells.

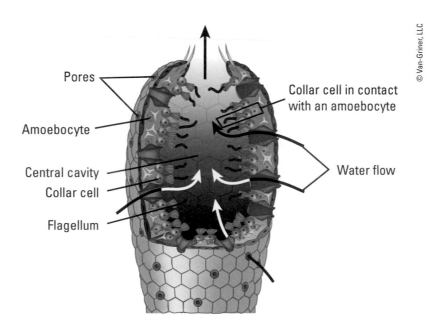

Pores

Amoebocyte

Central cavity

Collar cell

Flagellum

Collar cell in contact with an amoebocyte

Water flow

© Van-Griner, LLC

Figure 11.3 Sponge Anatomy.

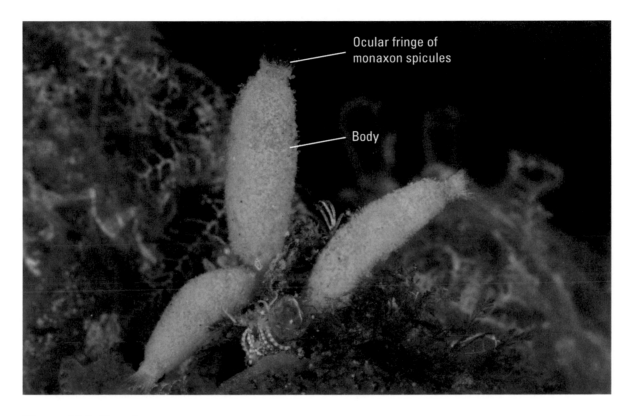

Figure 11.4 Scypha.

OBSERVE A CROSS SECTION SLIDE OF THE SPONGE SKELETON AND SPICULES

Try and locate the major structures found in a sponge, look closely for the choanocytes or collar cells. When looking at the sponge spicules, can you see why certain sponges are sold or made commercially for use in cleaning?

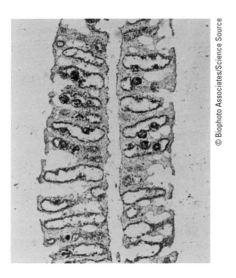

Figure 11.5 *Grantia* LM of Sponge. Light micrograph of the longitudinal section of a freshwater sponge (*Grantia* sp.).

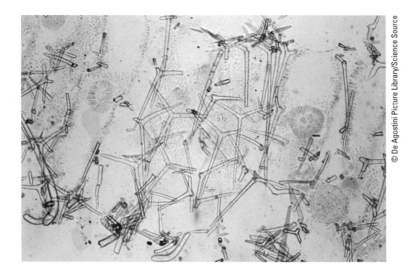

Figure 11.6 *Grantia* Sponge Spicules. Light micrograph (LM) of compressed *Grantia* sponge spicules, Grantiidae, seen under a microscope using normal light.

OBSERVE THE DIVERSITY OF SPONGES

There are thousands of species of sponges, most of them are living at the bottom of the sea floor, making sponges the most abundant animal found in that habitat. Some sponges are very small and some, like the giant barrel sponge, can reach a diameter of six feet. Some sponges can look as inconspicuous as a rock and some help bring beauty to coral reefs. Look at the samples of different sponges in lab and observe their diversity and how their differences can provide for success in their environments.

Figure 11.7 Fire Sponge. *Tedania ignis,* Caribbean.

Figure 11.8 Branching Tube Sponge. (*Pseudoceratina crassa*), Bahamas.

Figure 11.9 Giant Glass Barrel Sponge.

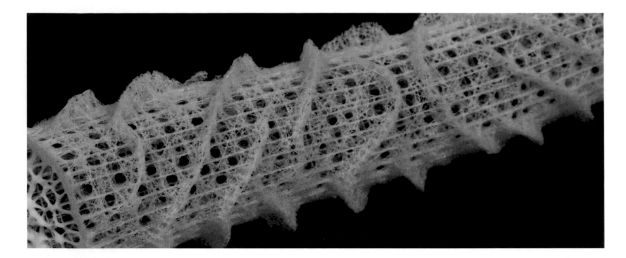

Figure 11.10 Glass Sponge. (*Euplectella*) skeleton, formed by silica spicules that unite into complex geometric structures.

PHYLUM CNIDARIA

Phylum Cnidaria consist of organisms such as jellyfish, anemones, and corals. Organisms in the Phylum Cnidaria live almost entirely in marine environments. Cnidarians are diploblastic, which means they contain two primary germ layers; the ectoderm and the endoderm. These organisms do not have specific organs or organ systems but are made of distinct tissues. Despite the lack of organs, Cnidarians are carnivorous organisms and are able to capture their prey with their specialized nervous tissue and special structures called nematocytes.

Nematocysts are specific structures found only in the Phylum Cnidaria. Nematocysts are microscopic stinging capsules or "stinging cells" that are concentrated by the thousands in each tentacle. Nematocysts are often barbed and contain venom and are used for capturing food and as a defense mechanism. Some species of Cnidarians are venomous enough to kill a human, such as the box jellyfish (*Chironex fleckeri*) found in Australia.

Cnidarians have two distinct body forms; the polyp and the medusa. The polyp body plan is primarily exhibited in sea anemones and consists of a cylindrical tube with its mouth facing upward. The polyp form usually attaches itself to a substrate such as a rock and anchors itself where it can grab food that passes by in the water. The medusa form, found in jellyfish, is free-swimming and umbrella shaped with its mouth found underneath surrounded by tentacles. While these two body plans look different, their basic morphology is very similar. Both the medusa and polyp body forms have mouths that are surrounded by tentacles and empty into a gastro-vascular cavity. Many Cnidarians are polymorphic and exhibit both body forms throughout their lifecycle. The mouth is the only opening in either cnidarian body plan, serving for both food intake and waste disposal.

Figure 11.11 Cnidarian Polyp Body Form. White Spotted Anemone, also known as Rose Anemone (*Urticina lofotensis*), Channel Islands, California.

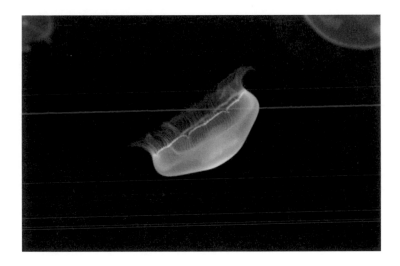

Figure 11.12 Cnidarian Medusa Body Form. Moon jellyfish (*Aurelia aurita*). This jellyfish, also known as the common jellyfish, is found in coastal waters throughout the world.

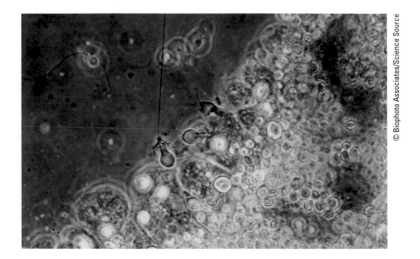

Figure 11.13 Nematocyst of a Hydra. Light micrograph of the compressed tentacle of a hydra (*Hydra* sp.) showing nematocysts, the venomous source of Cnidarian stings.

The Cnidarian life cycle involves an alternation between the medusa and polyp forms. Often the medusa form produces and releases eggs and sperm in the water for fertilization. After fertilization, a zygote develops into a swimming mass of ciliated larvae. Eventually, the larva anchors itself to a substrate and develops into a polyp. Polyps are able to reproduce asexually by budding or may continue the sexual cycle by budding an immature medusa which then develops into a mature medusa form.

Class Anthozoa, Hydrozoa, and Scyphozoa are the three traditional classes of Cnidarians. Class Cubozoa and Staurozoa are more recent classes of the phylum that have been recognized. In lab, we will primarily look at the anthozoans, hydrozoans, and scyphozoans.

CLASS ANTHOZOA—SEA ANEMONES AND CORALS

This is the largest class of the Cnidarians and consists of organisms that have the polyp body form and exist solitarily or as colonial organisms. Members of the Class Anthozoa are the sea anemones, stony corals, sea fans, sea whips, sea pens, and sea pansies. Anthozoan body form has a mouth that leads to a tubular pharynx with a gastrovascular cavity that is compartmentalized.

Sea anemones (pronounced ah-neh-moh-nees) are highly muscular and live in primarily sea water of all depths. Many corals have a symbiotic relationship with other organisms such as clownfish. The anemone provides shelter against predators and the clownfish feed off of invertebrates found in the anemone that could cause harm. The clownfish also produces fecal waste which is nourishment for the anemone.

Corals also exhibit symbiotic relationships with a photosynthetic dinoflagellate called **zooxanthellae.** Corals give zooxanthellae a home and the zooxanthellae provide coral with food. Most coral reefs are made primarily of hard corals. These corals are structurally similar to sea anemones, but smaller in size. Polyps of coral excrete an exoskeleton of calcium carbonate. Coral reefs are built upon these calcium carbonate skeletons and eventually can become one of the most diverse and beautiful ecosystems on Earth.

Figure 11.14 Anemone with Clownfish.

Figure 11.15 Sea Fan on Reef.

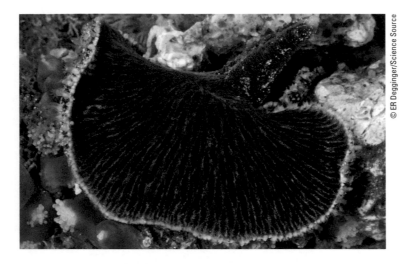

Figure 11.16 Koelliker's Sea Pansy. *Renilla koellikeri* Pacific Ocean, California.

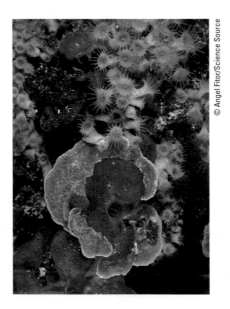

Figure 11.17 Coral Reef. Yellow cluster anemones (*Parazoanthus axinellae*) and various sponges (Phylum Porifera) on the wall of an underwater cave. Photographed in the Mediterranean Sea, Spain.

Figure 11.18 Brain Coral.

OBSERVE *METRIDIUM*

Metridium, is an example of a common anemone. Observe its mouth and tentacles.

Figure 11.19 Frilled *Metridium.* Mouth of Frilled *Metridium* Anemone (*Metridium senile*).

OBSERVE SAMPLES OF CORALS

Observe samples of corals provided in lab. These samples have lost their pigments due to the zooxanthellae that is no longer alive or present within the coral. This breakdown of the zooxanthellae is referred to as coral bleaching. Without the zooxanthellae and their symbiotic relationship with the coral, the coral eventually dies and all that is left is a calcium carbonate ($CaCO_3$) skeleton.

Figure 11.20 Bleached Coral. This coral has been bleached due to the loss of symbiotic algae. The exact mechanism or trigger for the bleaching is unknown, but adverse changes in the coral's environment are factors. Increases in sea temperatures due to global warming and sea pollution have both been cited as probable causes for the death of corals.

CLASS CUBOZOA

Class Cubozoa contain box jellies. These organisms are box like and have tentacles hanging from the corners of the box. Box jellies are vicious predators and very strong swimmers, some have image forming eyes. The Australian box jelly (*Chironex fleckeri*) is known to have such a lethal sting that it can kill humans.

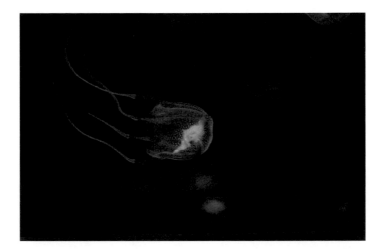

Figure 11.21 Box Jellyfish. (*Chironex fleckeri*) This species of jellyfish, also known as the sea wasp, belongs to the cubozoa order of invertebrates. It has a cube-shaped bell (main body) that grows up to 30 centimeters in diameter and four groups of tentacles on each corner. The tentacles are lined with stinging nematocysts that are used to kill fish and crustaceans. The nematocysts contain a venom that causes severe pain, nausea, vomiting, and respiratory problems in humans. In many cases death can result.

CLASS HYDROZOA

Hydras for the most part exhibit both the medusa and polyp stages in their life cycle. Most species are colonial and all have a sedentary polyp form as adults. Some polyps in a colony may be specialized for feeding while others may be specialized for reproduction. The infamous Portuguese Man-of-War (*Physalia physalis*) is not a jellyfish common to popular belief, but a colony of polyp and medusa individual hydrozoans.

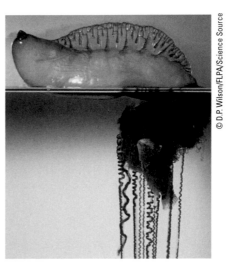

© D.P. Wilson/FLPA/Science Source

Figure 11.22 Portuguese Man-of-War. (*Physalia physalis*)

OBSERVE *HYDRA*

1. *Hydra* are small hydrozoans that live in shallow freshwater. *Hydra* lack a medusa stage and are very small in size.

2. Observe living *Hydra,* if available. Place in a small Petri dish and observe its behaviors under a dissecting microscope. Observe how *Hydra* respond to stimuli such as movement and food (such as brine shrimp).

3. Observe microscope slides of *Hydra,* if available. Look at the internal structures at the cellular level.

© Van-Griner, LLC

Figure 11.23 *Hydra* Ingesting a Copepod. These animals have typical cnidarian features: radial symmetry, saclike bodies with only one opening, and stinging tentacles for catching prey. They spend their entire lives as sedentary polyps and are hermaphrodites, where each hydra has testes on its stalk that can fertilize any eggs. When conditions are good the *Hydra* can also reproduce asexually, with young simply budding from the adult's body.

OBSERVE *OBELIA* SLIDE

Obelia exist in both polyp and medusa forms. Medusae reproduce sexually and the polyp form is able to reproduce by budding.

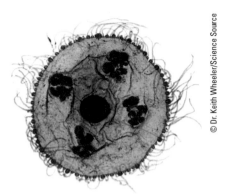

Figure 11.24 *Obelia* Medusa. Light micrograph of a single specimen of the medusa stage of a colonial marine invertebrate, the sea fir *Obelia geniculata.* Similar in appearance to a jellyfish, this is the free-swimming stage, released from the sessile, stalked, colonial polyp stage. Each medusa has a ring of solid tentacles all with a swelling at their base. Within the medusa are structures such as statocysts, canals, and gonads, all grouped symmetrically (four of these groupings are seen here at right angles). The central structure (round) is called the manubrium, and has oral tentacles. Magnification: 7× when printed at 10 cm wide.

Figure 11.25 LM of *Obelia* Hydrozoa Polyps. Magnification: 25× when printed at 10 cm.

OBSERVE *PHYSALIA* (PORTUGUESE MAN-OF-WAR)

Can you distinguish the different medusa and polyp forms? Some polyps fill with gas and allow the colony to float which gives *Physalia* its jelly-like appearance.

Figure 11.26 Tentacles of Portuguese Man-of-War. Tentacles of a Portuguese Man-of-War (*Physalia* sp.) collected from the surf zone of the beach at Port Aransas, Texas. Dark, highly folded tentacles sting and haul up prey; lighter tentacles are zooids specialized for feeding.

OBSERVE *GONIONEMUS*

1. In order to see *Gonionemus* well, you may need to float it in a beaker of water and observe it under a dissecting microscope. *Gonionemus* is a hydrozoan with a large medusae. Be able to located the different parts of the medusa form.

2. Find the following structures on *Gonionemus.*

   a. **Manubrium**—Stalk-like structure that hangs down from the center. Mouth attaches at the end of the manubrium.

   b. **Mouth**

   c. **Tentacles**—House batteries of nematocysts

   d. **Ovaries or gonads**—Attached to radial canals

   e. **Radial and ring canals**

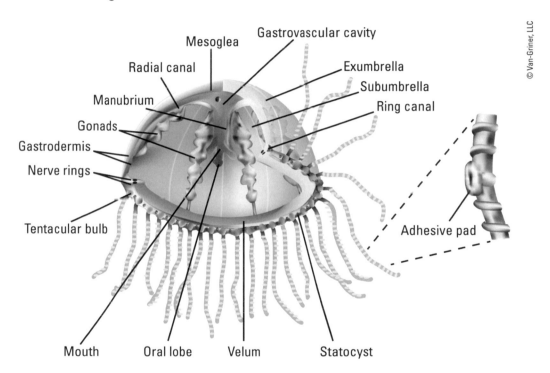

Figure 11.27 Illustration of Basic Structures of *Gonionemus*.

CLASS *SCYPHOZOA*

Commonly known as the jellyfish, scyphozoans spend the majority of their life cycle in a gelatinous medusa form. The polyp form occurs during their larval stage. The gastrovascular cavity is divided into four sections and the majority of scyphozoans are colorless. The epithelium around the outer ring of the jellyfish contains muscle cells that alternately contract and relax propelling itself through the water.

The species *Cyanea capillota* or the Lion's mane jellyfish is considered to be one of the largest invertebrates in the world and can grow to a diameter of two meters.

Figure 11.28 Lion's Mane Jellyfish. (*Cyanea capillata*). Lion's mane jellyfish are the largest known species of jellyfish. They can reach over two meters across with tentacles of around 30 meters long, containing millions of nematocysts (stinging cells). They range from Arctic waters to the coasts of Florida, USA, and Mexico.

OBSERVE *AURELIA* (MOON JELLYFISH)

Figure 11.29 Moon Jellyfish.

OBSERVE *CASSIOPEIA*

OBSERVE PREPARED SLIDES OF *AURELIA* EPHYRA, PLANULA LARVAE, AND SCYPHOSTOMA

CLASS STAUROZOA

This small class known as the star jellies were previously in the class Scyphozoa but were differentiated because although these organisms resemble a medusa body plan in most ways, it attaches itself to a substrate by a stalk that forms opposite its mouth.

PHYLUM PLATYHELMINTHES

Phylum Platyhelminthes are the first organisms in the animal kingdom to have bilateral symmetry. This change in body plan from radial symmetry has allowed for higher levels of specialization in some areas of their body, such as the head.

Platyhelminthes are soft bodied and flattened dorsal-ventrally. They are often called flat worms because of this flattening. Flatworms are free living and occur in a variety of environments including salt and fresh water and in moist terrestrial habitats.

Movement occurs by use of ciliated cells that surround their bodies on their ventral (or underside) surface and through well-developed musculature. Food is obtained through capturing prey and scavenging, however, some species such as the tapeworm are parasitic and live inside a host. Like Cnidarians, digestion begins and ends in the mouth, which is the only opening to the external environment. Platyhelminthes also contain a mesoderm in addition to an ectoderm and endoderm, making flatworms the first group of organisms that have three germ layers, or triploblastic. Classes of the Phylum Platyhelminthes include Tubellaria, Trematoda, and Cestoda.

CLASS TURBELLARIA

Turbellarians include free-living flatworms that are found in saltwater and freshwater or moist terrestrial environments. Organisms from this class are hermaphroditic and have both male and female sex organs.

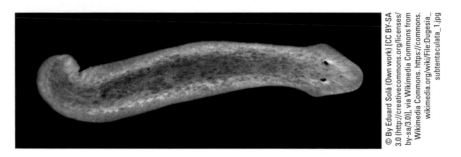

Figure 11.30 Brown Planaria. Light micrograph of Brown Planaria (*Dugesia tigrina*), a common flatworm.

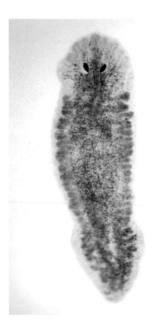

Figure 11.31 LM of a Planaria.

OBSERVE *DUGESIA*

Dugesia is a common freshwater flatworm or planaria.

1. Using a dissecting microscope locate the eyespot and pharynx on the outer anatomy on a living planaria (or *Dugesia*) and note *Dugesia's* movement and feeding behaviors with cooked eggs or cat food. Experiment with how planaria react to different stimuli such as light or touch.

2. Look at microscope slides of the cross sections and long sections of planaria that illustrate internal structures such as the gastrovascular cavity and the endoderm, mesoderm, and ectoderm (or epidermis).

CLASS TREMATODA—FLUKES

Trematodes are commonly called flukes. Trematodes are parasitic and feed on their hosts both externally and internally by suckers, hooks, and anchors. Flukes, once inside their host through organisms such as snails or fish, generally stay in their host for the majority of their life cycle.

Fasciola hepatica, the sheep liver fluke, infects sheep and other vertebrates. Another Trematode, *Schistosoma* causes Schistosomiasis, a common disease in many tropical countries with poor water quality. These flukes are very hard to get rid of because of their location and they do not have an easy route out of the body through the urogenital system. They also lay hundreds of eggs per day.

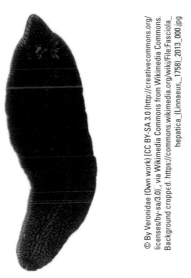

Figure 11.32 Giant Liver Fluke, *Fasciola hepatica.* Light micrograph of a giant liver fluke, *Fasciola hepatica,* a parasite of sheep, cattle, and humans. Humans ingest the encysted larvae through eating watercress and water chestnuts. Immature flukes migrate through the duodenum and into the bile ducts via the liver, where they reach maturity and lay eggs. These are passed in feces which may contaminate lakes and streams. The eggs then hatch to release free-swimming larvae which penetrate the soft tissues of their next hosts, snails. A free-swimming form released from the snails becomes encysted on aquatic vegetation, forming the next infective stage. Magnification unknown.

Figure 11.33 *Schistosoma mansoni.* Light micrograph of an adult male *Schistosoma mansoni,* a parasitic blood fluke that causes schistosomiasis (bilharzia). Fluke larvae live inside freshwater snails. The larvae leave their host when mature, and enter the water. They will penetrate human skin to reach the bloodstream, where they inhabit blood vessels of the intestine and bladder, releasing eggs into feces or urine to contaminate freshwater. This parasitic disease causes liver, kidney and bladder damage but can be treated with the drug praziquantel that kills the flukes. The female adult fluke (not visible) lives in a cleft below the male worm's head. Magnification 20× at 35 mm.

OBSERVE SLIDES OF *FASCIOLA HEPATICA* AND *SCHISTOSOMA*

CLASS CESTODA—TAPEWORMS

Known as tapeworms these organisms live their adult lives inside a host's intestines. They do not have a distinct head or a mouth or even a digestive cavity. Absorption of food occurs through their ectoderm.

There are three sections of a tapeworm's body: the anterior scolex, the neck, and the proglottids. The scolex is where the tapeworm attaches to its host with hooks and suckers. Between the scolex and the proglottids is the neck. Proglottids consist of repetitive sections of reproductive structures. The progottid section is relatively long compared to the neck and scolex. Each proglottid is a separate hermaphroditic section containing both male and female reproductive organs.

Figure 11.34 Human Tapeworm. A cestode, a parasitic tapeworm.

OBSERVE *TAENIA* PRESERVED SPECIMENS

Look for three specific segments found on the tapeworm: scolex, neck, and proglottids.

PHYLUM NEMATODA

Commonly referred to as roundworms, nematodes are pseudo-coelomates, which mean they have a cavity found in their mesoderm, but it is filled with fluid instead of being hollow. Hollow coeloms are found in organisms of higher phyla. In nematodes, the pseudo-coelom serves as a type of circulatory system and hydrostatic skeleton providing support for the organism. Muscles allow for movement around this skeleton. Nematodes are also the first phylum where its species have a distinct mouth and anus.

Nematodes survive in a variety of environments and many are parasitic. They range in size from microscopic to several feet long. Nematodes are bilaterally symmetrical and un-segmented. They have a thick waxy cuticle which protects them from their environment. Many nematodes cause disease in humans, such as Elephantiasis, in which nematodes infect a human host and clog the lymphatic system causing huge swelling of appendages. Since nematodes have a tough cuticle covering, they often find a successful homes in the digestive tract of humans.

OBSERVE *ASCARIS*

Ascaris is a large nematode that lives in the intestines of vertebrate animals, including humans. Males are smaller than females and have a hooked posterior end. The anus is also found on the posterior end.

1. Make sure to locate the mouth and anus and be able to differentiate between male and female.

2. Cut a female *Ascaris* longitudinally and pin the sides of the cuticle onto the dissection pan. The stringy structures found towards the posterior end are the ovaries.

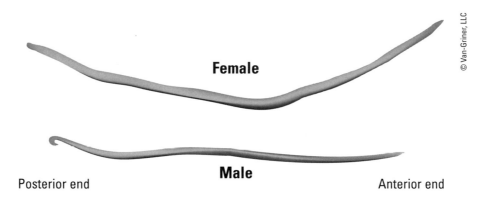

Figure 11.35 Illustration of Basic Structures of Ascaris.

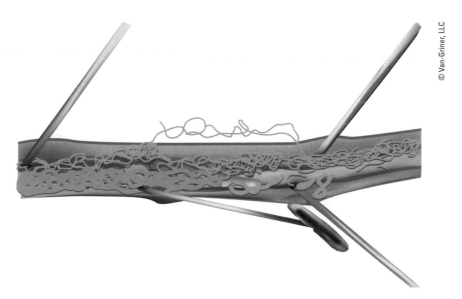

Figure 11.36 Close-Up Illustration of Dissection of Ascaris.

OBSERVE *TRICHINELLA*

Trichinella spiralis is a nematode that causes the disease trichinosis. Generally, if food such as pork or game is under cooked the larvae which is incased into the muscle of the meat is ingested and then finds a new home inside the host where it is able to mature. Symptoms of trichinosis include nausea, heartburn, and diarrhea and can potentially cause neurological problems.

1. Look at a slide with *Trichinella* larvae that is encapsulated in muscle tissue.

2. If available, look at adult *Trichinella* preserved specimens.

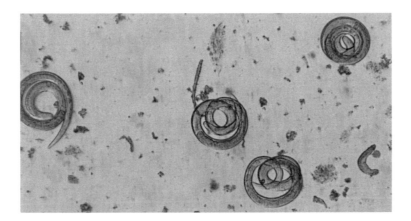

Figure 11.37 *Trichinella spiralis.* Light micrograph of *Trichinella spiralis,* a pork roundworm. Natural hosts for these nematodes are flesh eating animals such as humans, pigs, and rats. Trichinosis or *Trichinella* infections can occur when infected meat is not thoroughly cooked. Symptoms of infection include chest pain, diarrhea, myaglia, periorbital oedema, pyrexia, and trismus.

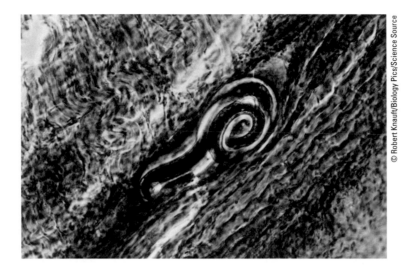

Figure 11.38 *Trichinella spiralis* **Larvae.** Light micrograph of *Trichinella spiralis,* a parasitic roundworm that causes trichinosis. The life cycle of the parasite begins when the infectious cysts are eaten with the flesh of a meat-eating animal. Trichinosis begins with the colonization of trichinella larvae in muscles where they grow. Migrating juveniles cause pain as they invade muscle tissue. Symptoms may include swelling, delirium, cardiac and pulmonary difficulty, pneumonia, nervous disorders, deafness, and delayed or lost reflexes. Nausea, dysentery, and colic are symptoms of adult worms. Magnification 64× at 35 mm.

PHYLUM MOLLUSCA

Mollusks are found in saltwater, freshwater, and moist terrestrial environments. They are the second most diverse phylum next to arthropods and include a diversity of organisms including: snails, slugs, clams, scallops, squid, and octopuses. Mollusks are the first coelomate organisms; they have a body cavity that is surrounded by the mesoderm and have complex organ systems.

Mollusks have a mantle, a thick epidermal sheet that secretes a calcium carbonate shell. Mollusks produce many types of shells, most of them are external, these shells provide for very diverse body forms throughout the phylum. Locomotion is provided by a muscular foot, which in some species are modified into tentacles. Mollusks can be predators and for the most part feed with a beak-like structure, called the **radula.** Organs are also more specialized in the Phylum Mollusca. They have a kidney-like structure for the removal of wastes called a **nephridium.** Through the nephridium, wastes are released through an excretory pore, not their mouth as in previous phyla discussed.

Mollusks are a very important source of food for humans and are used in a variety of other ways such as in jewelry and decorative objects. They can also serve as pests for humans such as zebra mussels, which can out compete other species and cause havoc to water treatment facilities. There are four classes found in the Phylum Mollusca: Class Polyplacophora, Class Gastropoda, Class Bivalvia, and Class Cephalopoda.

Figure 11.39 Zebra Mussels. *(Dreissena polymorpha)*, an invasive species now common in North America. Originally from the Black Sea, zebra mussels arrived in bilge water carried in cargo ships.

CLASS POLYPLACOPHORA—CHITONS

Chitons are found only in marine environments and have an ancient mollusk structure. They tend to be oval in shape and their dorsal side is covered with eight overlapping plates. They are herbivores that graze on the oceans' bottom scraping food off rocks with their radula. Some species can live in the harsh environments of the deepest depths.

Figure 11.40 Northern Red Chiton. *(Tonicella rubra)* Deer Island, New Brunswick, Canada. They are slow moving mollusks that graze on algae and breathe through gills.

OBSERVE CHITONS

Look at a preserved chiton and examine its external features. Locate the shell plates, mouth, foot, and gills.

CLASS GASTROPODA—SNAILS AND SLUGS

The Class Gastropoda (Gastro = stomach, poda = foot) include snails and slugs, which live in primarily marine and freshwater environments, but also are the only mollusks that are able to live on land. For the most part, gastropods have a single coiled shell that is often elaborate. Gastropods such as slugs and nudibranchs have a shell that is internal. Gastropods use their radula for feeding off of hard surfaces such as rocks. Nudibranchs; however, are able to get food through predatorial means.

Figure 11.41 Beaded Lancetooth Snail. (*Ancotrema sportella*), Quinault Valley, Olympic Peninsula, Washington. This snail is a predator of other snails and slugs. It occurs in forested habitats throughout western Washington.

Figure 11.42 California Banana Slug.

Figure 11.43 Nudibranch. *(Chromodoris kuniei)*

OBSERVE A VARIETY OF SAMPLE OF GASTROPODS PROVIDED IN LAB

CLASS BIVALVIA—CLAMS, MUSSELS, AND COCKLES

These organisms do not have a radula, like other mollusks. Bivalves are primarily filter feeders. Bivalves' shells are composed of two shells that are connected by a dorsal hinge. The mantles fuse together from each shell to form an incurrent siphon on the ventral side and an excurrent siphon that is located dorsally. Water flows through the incurrent siphon over gills where food particles are caught and moved by cilia toward the bivalve's mouth.

Figure 11.44 Atlantic Surf Clam. *Spisula solidissima* in the Gulf of Maine.

Figure 11.45 Quagga Mussels. Quagga Mussels (*Dreissena rostriformis bugensis*) are a freshwater species of bivalve mollusk indigenous to the Dnieper River in Ukraine. It is an invasive species in lakes and rivers of North America, with particular concern in the Great Lakes region. Like zebra mussels (*Dreissena polymorpha*), they are prolific breeders, and their colonies can clog and corrode water pipes. They filter phytoplankton from the water they inhabit, rendering the environment poor in nutrients for the rest of the food chain.

EXTERNAL AND INTERNAL BIVALVE ANATOMY

1. Obtain a bivalve provided in lab. Locate the external anterior and posterior ends of the bivalve. Locate the hinge and the anterior umbo.

2. Separate the two shells by using a scalpel to cut the adductor muscles and by pulling the two shells apart while resting the umbo on the dissecting tray.

3. Locate the following structures of the bivalve: umbo, mantle, gills, anterior and posterior adductor muscles, foot, mouth, labial palps, digestive gland, gonad tissue, and heart. Use Figure 11.46 to help.

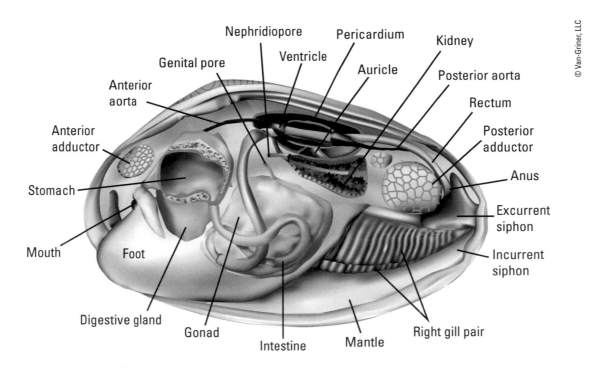

Figure 11.46 Anatomy of Clam.

CLASS CEPHALOPODA—SQUID, OCTOPUSES, NAUTILUSES, AND CUTTLEFISH

Class Cephalopoda (cephalo = head, poda = foot) include some of the most interesting organisms found in the oceans. Cephalopods live in strictly marine environments and in most species, their shell is greatly reduced and found internally. The foot in cephalopods are modified into tentacles which allows them to swim very fast and look as if they are jet propelling themselves through the water. Cephalopods are also different from other mollusks because they have a closed circulatory system.

Food is obtained through predatorial means, and cephalopods have a number of defense mechanisms that allow them to be very successful at catching prey and avoiding being preyed on. Cephalopods also have well developed eyes; the largest eyes of the animal kingdom belong to the giant squid and are the size of dinner plates. Cephalopods are also known for their intelligence and have the largest relative brain size of any of the invertebrates.

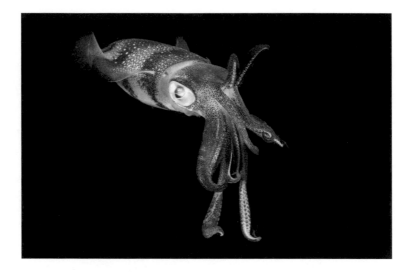

Figure 11.47 Big Fin Reef Squid. *Sepioteuthis lessoniana* adult at night.

Figure 11.48 Mimic Octopus.

Figure 11.49 Chambered Nautilus. *Nautilus pompilius*.

Figure 11.50 Cuttlefish.

OBSERVE SQUID

1. Externally, observe squid's eyes, mantle or body tube, arms, and tentacles.

2. Lay the squid flat on the dissecting tray, carefully cut the mantle open to reveal its internal organs. **Be careful of the ink sac, it can squirt!** Locate the pen, mouth, anus, hearts, ink sac, stomach, kidney, eyes, and reproductive structures.

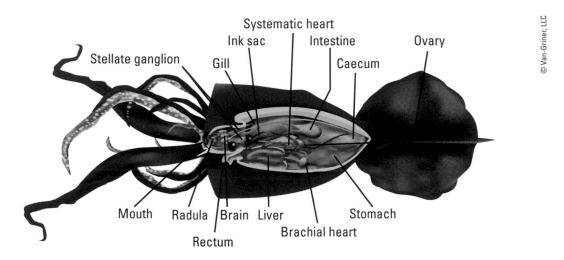

Figure 11.51 Internal Anatomy of Squid.

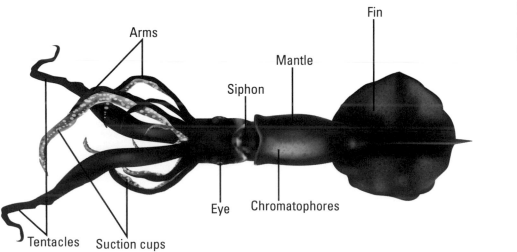

Figure 11.52 Anatomy of Squid.

OBSERVE MORE CEPHALOPODS

Look at other examples provided in lab of cephalopods, if available.

Biology 101 Laboratory Manual

LABORATORY 11 REVIEW
ANIMAL DIVERSITY, PART 1

QUESTIONS (15 POINTS)

1. What are the characteristics of the Kingdom Animalia?

_____

_____

2. What is the difference between diploblastic and triploblastic organisms? Give an example of each.

_____

_____

3. What are the characteristics of the Phylum Porifera?

_____

_____

4. Why are sponges considered an evolutionary dead end?

_____

_____

5. What are nematocysts? What organisms do they belong in and how are they used?

_____

_____

6. Differentiate between the medusa and polyp body forms in Cnidarians. Give examples of organisms that exhibit each.

_____

_____

7. What are the different characteristics of the Phylum Cnidaria?

_____

_____

8. Corals have a symbiotic relationship with what organism? Explain how the relationship works and give another example of a symbiotic relationship.

_____

_____

9. What are the characteristics of the Phylum Platyhelminthes?

_____

_____

10. Flatworms have distinct posterior and anterior ends. How does this affect their movement from previously discussed organisms like the sponges and Cnidarians?

_____

_____

11. What are the characteristics of the Phylum Mollusca?

_____

_____

12. What are the classes of Mollusca? Give an example of each and describe some of their characteristics.

_____

_____

13. In what ways does the shell found in a mollusk function like a skeleton found in an organism like a human?

_____

_____

14. Explain why cephalopods are such fierce predators.

_____

_____

15. Outline your favorite organism discussed in this lab. Identify its phylum, class, and specific characteristics.

_____

_____

NOTES

LABORATORY 12
ANIMAL DIVERSITY, PART 2

SURVEY OF THE ANIMAL KINGDOM CONTINUED—PHYLA ANNELIDA, ARTHROPODA, ECHINODERMATA, AND CHORDATA

LEARNING OBJECTIVES

■ Understand how organisms survive and succeed in their environment with specific structures and adaptations.

■ Recall key characteristics of the phyla and the characteristics of some of the classes that are in each.

■ Describe body forms and general life cycles of selected organisms in each phylum.

■ Identify specific structures from selected organisms in each phylum.

■ Classify selected animals into the correct phylum as well as correct class.

INTRODUCTION

In the previous lab exercise you learned about the fundamental characteristics of animals. The introductory survey to animals showed the principles and practices of developing a classification system and taxonomic key based on perceived evolutionary relationships. Remember, classification does not simply name an organism but provides clues that tell us something about the organism's relationships. Scientists place organisms into taxa with other organisms to which they are closely related. This results in different levels of classification, with taxa at the highest level being the largest. For example, last week you saw *Gonionemus,* a hydrozoan. How was it classified? Let's review how three animals from last week are classified:

Table 12.1 Review of Classification from Kingdom Animalia.

Taxa	Gonionemus	Planaria	Clam (Quahog)
Kingdom	Animalia	Animalia	Animalia
Phylum	Cnidaria	Platyhelminthes	Mollusca
Class	Hydrozoa	Turbellaria	Bivalvia
Order	Limnomedusae	Tricladida	Veneroida
Family	Olindiasidae	Planariidae	Veneridae
Genus	*Gonionemus*	*Planaria*	*Mercenaria*
Species	*hornelli*	*torva*	*mercenaria*

In this exercise today you will have the opportunity to view and classify new animals from the Phyla Annelida, Arthropoda, Echinodermata, and Chordata. Pay attention to the emergence of key features and characteristics absent from the first animal survey.

LAB ACTIVITIES

PHYLUM ANNELIDA, THE SEGMENTED WORMS

Earthworms and leeches are readily recognized and well known members of the Phylum Annelida. Annelids are noted for their distinctive soft and segmented bodies. The annelid body is repeatedly divided by grooves and annules into segments. Each segment contains parts of the closed circulatory, digestive, nervous, and excretory systems. Annelids are the first animals to develop a true body cavity. One external characteristic of annelids is setae, small, bristlelike appendages typically found in pairs on either the lateral or ventral surfaces. A variation in this characteristic is a distinctive feature for all three classes of annelids. The three classes are Polychaeta, Oligochaeta, and Hirudinea.

© By Leslie H. Harris [CC BY 3.0 (http://creativecommons.org/licenses/by/3.0)], via Wikimedia Commons from Wikimedia Commons. https://commons.wikimedia.org/wiki/File:Oxydromus_pugetensis.jpg

Figure 12.1 Polychaeta.

Figure 12.2 Oligochaeta. Marine worm, *Nereis* sp.

Figure 12.3 Hirudinea.

CLASS POLYCHAETA (*POLY* = MANY, *CHAETA* = SETAE), BRISTLE WORMS

Nereis, a marine clam worm, is perfectly adapted for living in sediment. A close look at the polychaete's anatomy reveals a heavily segmented body with each segment bearing a pair of fleshy appendages called parapodia. Parapodia assist in the movement and respiration of the worm due to their large surface area containing highly vascularized blood vessels. Many setae can be found protruding from the parapodia as well. Modification of the parapodia and presence of many setae is a defining characteristic that led to the class name.

Figure 12.4 *Aphrodita.* Polychaete marine worm. Polychaetes are a class of annelid (segmented) worms. Each segment has a pair of fleshy un-jointed limb-like appendages (parapodia) which aid in locomotion and act as external gills. This specimen was found at a depth of 500 meters, on the Bellingshausen Sea continental shelf, Antarctica.

OBSERVE SEVERAL POLYCHAETES

1. Obtain preserved specimens of *Nereis, Aphrodita,* and *Chaetopterus.* What do these worms have in common? Look closely at the highly modified parapodia and presence of setae.

2. Examine a prepared slide of parapodium.

3. Sketch the parapodium and bristles.

CLASS OLIGOCHAETA (*OLIGO* = FEW OR SMALL, *CHAETA* = SETA)

The most common and familiar oligochaete is the earthworm, *Lumbricus terrestris.* This class of worms can be found in terrestrial and freshwater habitats scavenging for food. The segmented body lacks parapodia and typically few setae are present. Movement through soil is achieved by alternating contractions of circular and longitudinal muscles. This is not an undulating motion but rather a slow extension, anchoring, and contraction. Recall that this phylum lacks a rigid skeleton and instead uses a hydrostatic (water pressure) support system for muscles to pull against. Earthworms are hermaphroditic, meaning each worm produces egg and sperm cells. A prominent external feature of earthworms is a series of swollen segments known as the clitellum. When copulating, earthworms attach by joining their clitella to exchange sperm. The earthworms separate and the clitellum secretes a mucus that slides down the worm picking up eggs and stored sperm. Once the eggs are fertilized the worm releases the mucus band as a cocoon.

© By Jackhynes at English Wikipedia (Own work) [Public domain], via Wikimedia Commons from Wikimedia Commons. https://commons.wikimedia.org/wiki/ File:Mating_earthworms.jpg

Figure 12.5 Earthworm Copulation. Like most other worms, they are hermaphroditic, having both male and female reproductive organs. Most worms must still mate with another of their species in order to reproduce. When two worms or crawlers mate, they lie alongside one another, and both transfer sperm to each other. Each will lay one or more capsules of eggs from which will emerge one or two fully-formed tiny worms. The familiar thickened "band" near the front end of most worms is a structure called the clitellum which secretes mucus and other substances that form the capsule containing the fertilized eggs.

OBSERVE EXTERNAL ANATOMY OF EARTHWORMS

1. Obtain a preserved *Lumbricus* and examine the external features. How is the earthworm different from the clamworm, *Nereis?*

2. Use a dissecting microscope to determine the number and arrangement of any setae.

3. Locate the earthworm's clitellum, genital pores, mouth, and anus.

OBSERVE INTERNAL ANATOMY OF EARTHWORMS

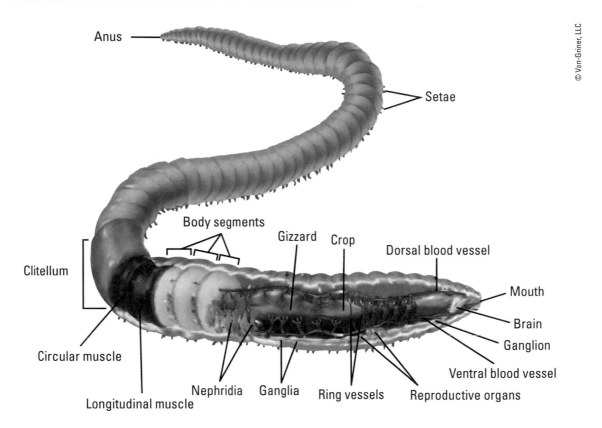

Figure 12.6 External and Internal Anatomy of an Earthworm.

CLASS HIRUDINEA

Hirudineans, like leeches, live in marine, freshwater, and terrestrial habitats. Leeches are not heavily segmented like *Nereis* or *Lumbricus* and have no parapodia or setae. Leeches can be found free-living (carnivorous) or parasitic. One other discernible difference is the presence of anterior and posterior suckers. Suckers function to hold prey while fluid is extracted. Leeches reproduce sexually and are hermaphroditic, too, like earthworms.

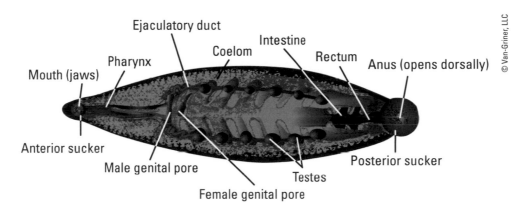

Figure 12.7 Leech.

OBSERVE PRESERVED LEECHES

1. Obtain a preserved leech and examine the external features.

2. Locate the two suckers. Which one is posterior?

3. Draw and record observations.

PHYLUM ARTHROPODA, (*ARTHRO* = JOINTED, *PODA* = FOOT OR APPENDAGE)

Phylum Arthropoda (arthropods) is the largest and most successful of the animal phyla. The diversity and abundance of arthropods can be seen in every environment from marine, freshwater, and terrestrial habitats. All arthropods have segmented bodies divided into a head, jointed legs, and abdomen. What allowed for this unprecedented success? The rigid external skeleton (exoskeleton) made of chitin and jointed appendages adapted for locomotion, feeding, reproduction, defense, and sensing their environment have allowed this phylum to exploit every niche. The exoskeleton isn't a real skeleton but may be hardened like a shell to protect the body. The exoskeleton serves as a site for muscle attachment and creates a moisture barrier. The exoskeleton may be shed at which time the animal rapidly grows before the new exoskeleton hardens. Classification of arthropods focuses on the arrangement of these segments and appendage structure.

SUBPHYLUM CHELICERATA

Chelicerates are arthropods with the appendages of their most anterior segment modified into chelicerae or feeding structures. Spiders, scorpions, and horseshoe crabs are easily recognized examples. The second pair of appendages called pedipalps assist in capturing prey, sensing the environment, or involved in copulation. The body segments are fused into two body regions: a cephalothorax and abdomen. There are no antennae.

CLASS MEROSTOMATA (HORSESHOE CRABS)

Limulus, horseshoe crabs, are ancient marine chelicerates that evolved over 500 million years ago during the Cambrian period. Horseshoe crabs have changed very little since the age of dinosaurs! The cephalothorax is covered by a horseshoe-shaped carapace and separated from the abdomen by a flexible joint. There are five pairs of walking legs and modified abdominal appendages called book gills (where gas exchange occurs).

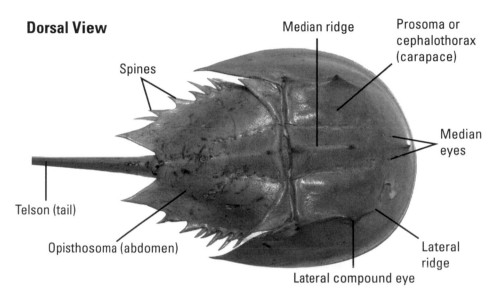

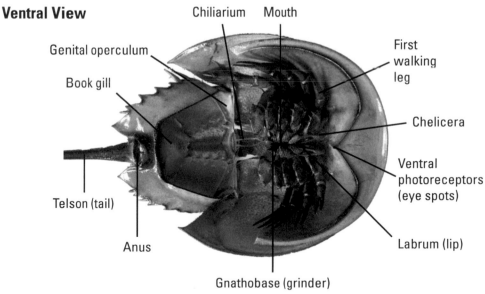

Figure 12.8 Horseshoe Crab. Dorsal and ventral views of a horseshoe crab, *Limulus.*

CLASS ARACHNIDA (SCORPIONS, TICKS, MITES, DADDY LONGLEGS, AND SPIDERS)

The most diverse class of chelicerates is the terrestrial arachnids. Chelicerae of the cephalothorax are modified into fangs to pierce prey. The pedipalps are used to manipulate food and sense the environment. There are four pairs of walking legs. One of the oldest living examples is the scorpion. The scorpion was one of the first terrestrial arthropods and evolved 425 million years ago during the Silurian period. The segments of scorpions are not fused, unusual for chelicerates, which supports its ancient origin. Spiders are the most familiar example of arachnids. Spiders often prey on insects and relatively small invertebrates. Often, spiders are incorrectly labeled as an insect. Remember, spiders have two body regions not three. Spiders also have eight legs and insects have six legs. Spiders tend to make webs using silk released from spinnerets.

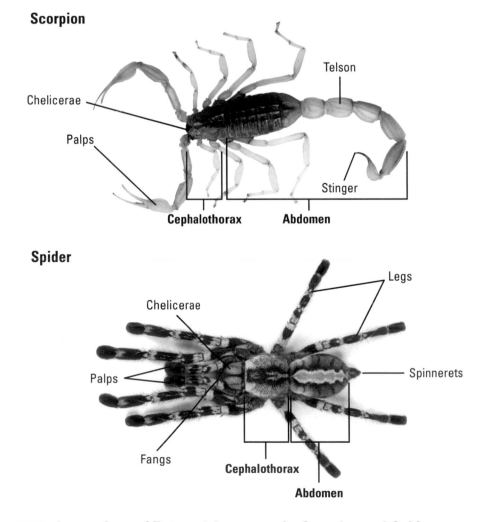

Figure 12.9 Comparison of External Anatomy of a Scorpion and Spider.

OBSERVE PRESERVED HORSESHOE CRABS, SPIDERS, AND SCORPIONS

1. Obtain a preserved specimen and examine the external features.

2. Identify the body regions: cephalothorax and abdomen for each specimen.

3. How does the segmentation of scorpions differ?

4. Where are the pedipalps? What are they modified for in each specimen?

5. How are the mouthparts (chelicerae) different?

6. How many appendages are there on each body segment?

7. Are the appendages jointed?

8. How many eyes are present?

SUBPHYLUM CRUSTACEA (CRAYFISH, CRABS, AND SHRIMP)

CLASS CRUSTACEA (CRAYFISH, CRABS, AND SHRIMP)

Crustaceans are the dominant aquatic arthropods and represent the second largest class. They are present in both freshwater and marine systems but the greatest diversity can be seen in the ocean. Morphologically, crustaceans are unique amongst the arthropods since members have biramous or double branched appendages, two pairs of antennae, and usually compound eyes with multiple lenses. Crustaceans and insects have opposing mandibles derived from an anterior appendage. The mandibles of crayfish are analogous to chelicerae of spiders. This means that the structures share the same function but are derived from different body segments. Homologous structures derived from the same body segment may be modified for different functions in different species. The same spider chelicerae are actually homologous to the crayfish antennae. The body parts of a crustacean are easily learned by examining a crayfish. The external anatomy of the crayfish shows the typical two regions and five pairs of modified appendages. The five anterior appendages are modified into first and second antennae, mandibles, maxillae, and maxillipeds. The four larger walking legs attach to the thorax and the smaller abdominal appendages are referred to as swimmerets or pleopods. The last pair of appendages is the broad, flat uropod surrounding the final abdominal segment called the telson.

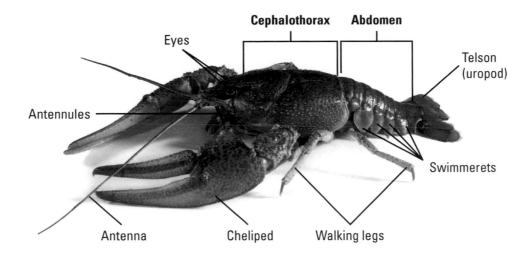

Figure 12.10 External Anatomy of Crayfish.

OBSERVE THE EXTERNAL ANATOMY OF A CRAYFISH

1. Obtain a preserved crayfish.

2. Locate the following external features: antenna, antennules, cheliped, rostrum, eyes, mouth, mixilliped, walking legs, carapace, cephalothorax, abdomen, swimmerets, anus, telson, and uropod.

3. Which body region is most heavily segmented?

4. Which appendages are biramous?

5. Determine how many legs are chelate (pincerlike with opposing claws).

6. Determine the sex of your crayfish.

OBSERVE THE INTERNAL ANATOMY OF A CRAYFISH

1. Make an incision on each side of the cephalothorax.

2. Cut across the base of the rostrum. Remove dorsal portion of carapace.

3. Locate three pairs of ostia on the heart. Remove the heart.

4. Locate the stomach, digestive glands, and gonads. Remove internal organs.

5. View the exposed end of the torn esophagus and anterior part of the ventral nerve cord. May need to remove musculature on the floor of the abdomen (tail) to see the nerve cord.

6. Locate the antennal glands. They are excretory organs found at the base of each antennae.

7. View any other internal features as directed by your instructor.

8. Dispose of specimen as specified by your instructor.

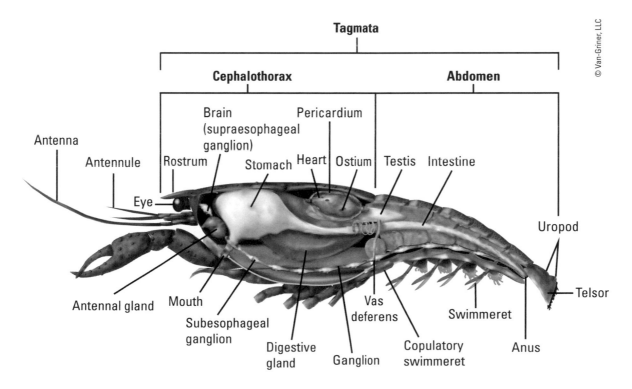

Figure 12.11 Internal Anatomy of a Crayfish.

SUBPHYLUM UNIRAMIA (CENTIPEDES, MILLIPEDES, AND INSECTS)

Classes belonging to the Subphylum Uniramia are all considered uniramous. They have opposing mandibles and single-branched appendages. Centipedes, millipedes, and insects belong under this classification.

CLASS CHILOPODA (CENTIPEDES)

Centipedes tend to be found living in soil, under logs, and even under rock where they prey on smaller arthropods. The centipede is designed to be a formidable predator. The dorsoventrally flattened body of a centipede possesses many segments each with one pair of legs. Having many legs allows the centipede to make fast and rapid movements. The first pair of legs is modified into venomous fangs sometimes called poison claws. The fangs are often mistaken for mandibles but are really modified maxillipeds for feeding. The mandibles are much smaller and located between the maxillipeds. The centipede is capable of delivering a fierce bite or wound.

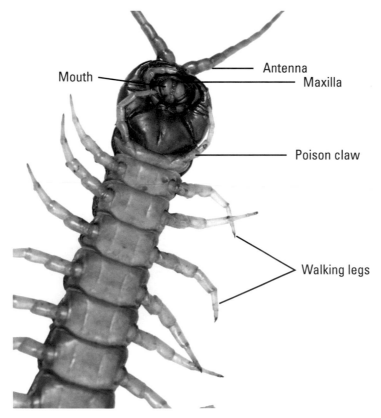

Figure 12.12 Centipede Maxilliped with Poison Fang. Stone centipede Jaws, *Lithobius forficatus*.

CLASS DIPLOPODA (MILLIPEDES)

Millipedes tend to exist in the same environments as centipedes and may be mistaken for one occasionally. Millipedes are not carnivorous and feed mainly on decaying plant matter. The round body of the millipede like that of a centipede has many body segments but each contains two pairs of legs. Millipedes travel slowly and are often seen curled up when disturbed to protect its soft underside. A foul-smelling odor can be observed from defensive millipedes. Each segment contains glands that secrete an offensive liquid to help protect it from predation.

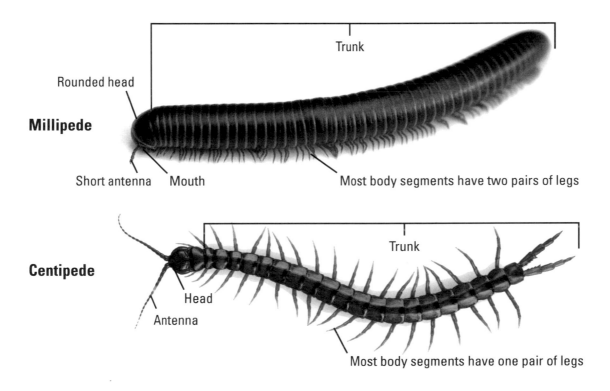

Figure 12.13 Comparison of External Anatomy between Centipede and Millipede.

EXTERNAL ANATOMY OF CENTIPEDES AND MILLIPEDES

1. Obtain preserved samples of centipedes and millipedes.

2. Compare and contrast the shape of the body and pairs of legs.

3. Find the centipede's first and second maxilla, maxillipeds, and antenna.

CLASS INSECTA (FLIES, GRASSHOPPERS, BUTTERFLIES, BEETLES, AND OTHERS)

Insects comprise nearly 75% of all known animals and are easily the largest group on Earth. Insects have three distinct body regions: head, thorax, and abdomen. There are one pair of antennae, six legs, and usually two pairs of wings on the thorax. Insects were the first animals to develop flight and the presence of wings were likely vital to their success. The wings are not modified appendages rather outgrowths of the thoracic exoskeleton. Another instrumental key feature of insects is the efficient respiratory system of tubes called tracheae that conduct air throughout the body. Another first to emerge with insects was a true form of communication. Insects display three types of communication ranging from sonic, visual, or chemical in nature. There are 26 orders of insects distinguished primarily by the structure of wings, mouthparts, and antennae. Typical characteristics of insects can be seen by studying a grasshopper, *Romalea*.

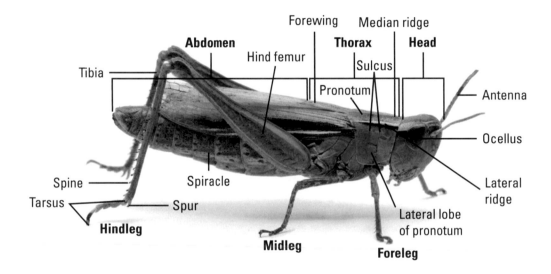

Figure 12.14 External Anatomy of an Adult Grasshopper.

EXTERNAL ANATOMY OF A GRASSHOPPER, *ROMALEA*

1. Obtain a preserved grasshopper specimen.

2. Locate the following external features: head, thorax, abdomen, antennae, mandibles, maxilla with maxillary palp, legs, and spiracles.

3. How many abdominal segments are present? What is found on each segment?

IDENTIFY SELECTED ORGANISMS USING A DICHOTOMOUS KEY

1. Obtain a jar with multiple preserved insects.

2. Using a dichotomous key (provided by your instructor) identify the order of each specimen.

Table 12.1 Major Characteristics of Classes of Phylum Arthropoda.

	Merostomata	Arachnida	Crustacea	Chilopoda	Diplopoda	Insecta
Names of Body Regions						
Number of Legs						
Arrangement of Legs						
Segmentation						
Number of Antennae						
Names of Major Sensory Organs						
Names of Major Mouth Parts						

PHYLUM ECHINODERMATA (*ECHINO* = SPINY, *DERM* =SKIN), SAND DOLLARS, SEA URCHINS, AND SEA STARS

Figure 12.15 Sand Dollar.

Figure 12.16 Sea Urchin.

Figure 12.17 Sea Star.

The last two phyla in today's survey are Echinodermata and Chordata—both of which are considered deuterostomes. Deuterostomes are a major break from the previous origins of animals discussed so far. Annelids, mollusks, and arthropods belonged to the line called protostomes. The difference between the two lines involves the development of the embryonic stage. The blastopore (opening to the first cavity formed in a developing embryo) of deuterostomes gives rise to the anus not the mouth. Refer to your text and Figure 12.18 for a detailed comparison between protostomes and deuterostomes.

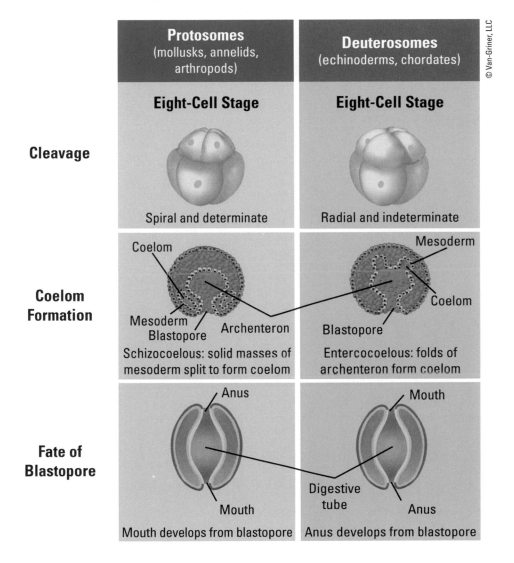

Figure 12.18 Protostomes Compared to Deuterostomes.

Most living adult echinoderms are radially symmetrical and their bodies are pentameral (i.e., they have fivefold symmetry) however, the larvae exhibit bilateral symmetry. Echinoderms typically are bottom-dwellers in marine habitats. Sea stars, brittle stars, sea urchins, and sand dollars are a few represented in today's class. The skin of echinoderms is thin, but covers hard, calcium-based plates that are often spiny. These plates are called ossicles and are used to distinguish between the five classes of echinoderms. Echinoderms have an internal canal system that forms "sucker or tube feet" at the end aiding in the exchange of nutrients, movement, and respiration. This unique water vascular system relies on muscle contractions and hydrostatic pressure to move the feet which move the animal. No other groups of animals possess this characteristic. Not exclusive to echinoderms is their great ability at regenerating damaged or lost body parts.

CLASS ASTEROIDEA (SEA STARS)

Sea stars are known to be predators within their environment and prey on oysters and clams. Sea stars use their arms and tube feet to grip the shell and apply enough pressure to pry it open. Once the prey is open sea stars evert their stomach inside to digest and engulf the tissue. The common sea star belongs to the class Asteroidea and has ossicles arranged loosely under the skin. The spines are small and tend to be blunt. The five arms of *Asterias* tend to be continuous with the central disk. The lower oral surface contains a centrally located mouth while the anus is on the upper aboral surface. The madreporite also is located on the aboral surface and acts like a sieve between the water vascular system and the environment. Dermal gills used for respiration surround the spines.

OBSERVE THE EXTERNAL ANATOMY OF THE COMMON SEA STAR, *ASTERIAS*

1. Look at a prepared slide of the bipinnaria larval stage of sea star development. Note the bilateral symmetry.

2. Working with a lab partner, obtain a preserved specimen of *Asterias*.

3. Examine the oral surface of the sea star and locate the following: central mouth and tube feet.

4. Use a dissecting microscope to take a closer look at the spines.

5. Examine the aboral surface of the sea star. Use a probe to touch the madreporite. What is the consistency?

OBSERVE THE INTERNAL ANATOMY OF THE COMMON SEA STAR, *ASTERIAS*

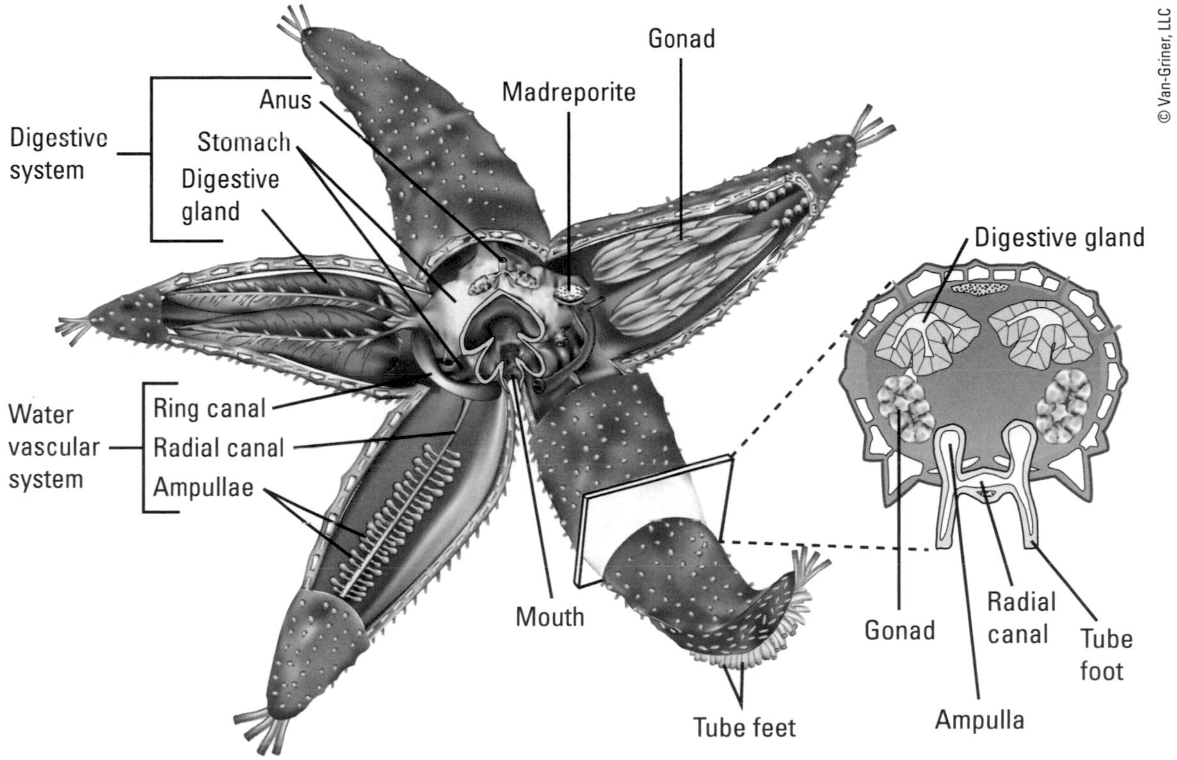

Figure 12.19 Diagram of the Internal Structure of a Sea Star.

CLASS OPHIUROIDEA (BRITTLE STARS)

Brittle stars are similar to sea stars except they have five long, slender, snake-like arms that are quite fragile. The arms are clearly demarcated from the central disk or body. The spines tend to be on the side of the arms and tube feet are greatly reduced in size. The flexible nature of brittle star arms extends to faster movement. Brittle stars tend to crawl like an octopus as opposed to the slower creep of a sea star. Brittle stars do not pry open prey rather they eat suspended food particles captured by tube feet and passed to their mouth.

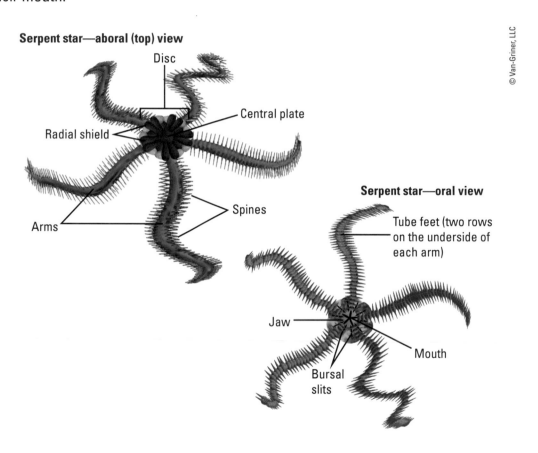

Figure 12.20 Serpent Star.

CLASS CRINOIDEA (SEA LILIES AND FEATHER STARS)

Crinoids are considered the most ancient echinoderms with only a few genera existing today. Extinct forms attached to a substrate via a stalk and were more similar to plants. Modern species today are not bound permanently to the substrate. Notice any unusual characteristics when observing a prepared crinoid? Crinoids differ from the previous echinoderms in that their oral surface (mouth and anus) faces up. Note the developed ossicles and highly branched, feathery arms. Crinoids are considered filter feeders and capture food particles on the mucus of their tube feet.

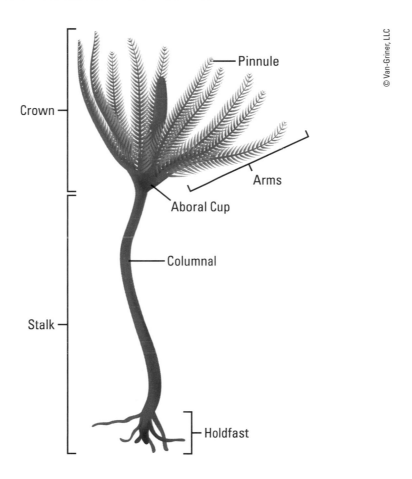

Figure 12.21 Parts of a Crinoid. Rosy featherstar (*Antedon bifida*) pentacrinoid larva.

CLASS ECHINOIDEA (SEA URCHINS AND SAND DOLLARS)

Sea urchins are well recognized by their oval-ball-shaped bodies covered with long, moveable spines. When held, note the flattened bottom compared to the domed surface. Urchins lack arms. Under the skin, close-fitting skeletal plates (ossicles) form a hard shell called a test. This test protects the animal's soft body that is hidden underneath. Like sea stars, urchins use their spines to crawl in a slow series of wavy rhythms. Crawling is achieved by depressing the forward spines and pushing with the backward spines. The tentacle like tube feet also plays a role in the urchin's locomotion. Speed is not a concern of urchins which prey on fixed algae, plankton, and dead material scavenged from their surroundings. The underside contains a mouth with teeth to scrape the algae off rocks. The movable jaw parts form a structure called Aristotle's Lantern.

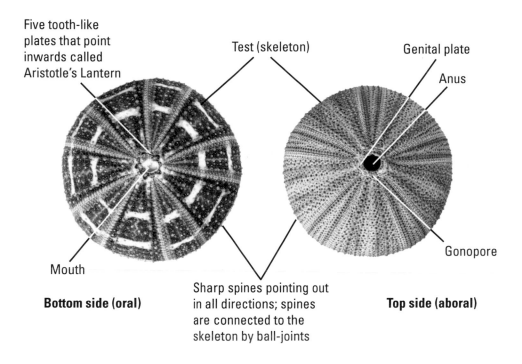

Five tooth-like plates that point inwards called Aristotle's Lantern

Test (skeleton)

Genital plate

Anus

Mouth

Bottom side (oral)

Sharp spines pointing out in all directions; spines are connected to the skeleton by ball-joints

Gonopore

Top side (aboral)

Figure 12.22 Sea Urchin Anatomy.

Sand dollars are specialized sea urchins adapted for burrowing just beneath the sand. The animal's body is flattened but still composed of a rigid skeleton, the test. The white disks washed up on beaches no longer have the skin with movable spines. Living sand dollars look very different. A soft, velvety skin that is dark in color covers the test. The spines of sand dollars are softer and smaller compared to other sea urchins. Sand dollars move with their tiny spines but not tube feet, which assist in breathing. On a sand dollar test, there is usually a pattern that looks like the petals of a flower. That pattern is made up of many tiny holes, and it is through these holes that the sand dollar's tube feet come out on top. On the underside of a sand dollar, there is a star pattern spreading out from the center where the mouth is. This star pattern is made up of food grooves. Sand dollars filter sand and water, catching plankton and other things on their spines. Cilia move the food into a food groove which leads to the mouth. Sand dollars are known to eat larvae of crustaceans, copepods, diatom, algae, and detritus.

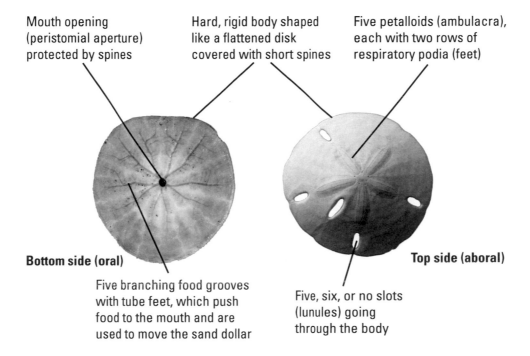

Mouth opening (peristomial aperture) protected by spines

Hard, rigid body shaped like a flattened disk covered with short spines

Five petalloids (ambulacra), each with two rows of respiratory podia (feet)

Bottom side (oral)

Top side (aboral)

Five branching food grooves with tube feet, which push food to the mouth and are used to move the sand dollar

Five, six, or no slots (lunules) going through the body

Figure 12.23 Sand Dollar Anatomy.

OBSERVE A PRESERVED SEA URCHIN AND SAND DOLLAR

1. Obtain a preserved urchin and sand dollar.

2. Compare and contrast the sand dollar's test of fused ossicles to an urchin's test.

3. If available, examine a dissected Aristotle's Lantern.

4. Locate the mouth of the urchin. Do you find teeth?

5. Compare the bleached test of a sand dollar to a preserved specimen.

CLASS HOLOTHUROIDEA (SEA CUCUMBERS)

The soft body of sea cucumbers sets them visually apart from other echinoderms. Note the body axis is oriented horizontally and radial symmetry is less evident. The ossicles aregreatly reduced as is the presence of spines. The mouth at one end of the animal is surrounded by modified tube feet called tentacles. Mucus secreted by the tentacles captures small floating organisms, which they eat.

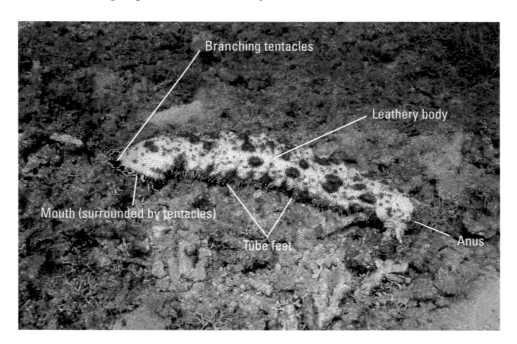

Figure 12.24 Sea Cucumber Anatomy.

OBSERVE A PRESERVED SEA CUCUMBER

1. Obtain a preserved sea cucumber.

2. Which end do you find the mouth?

3. What is the orientation of radial symmetry? Body axis?

PHYLUM CHORDATA

Chordata is the animal phylum with which most students are familiar since it includes humans and other vertebrates. Chordates include over 42,500 species of fish, amphibians, birds, and mammals. Common to the group is an internal bony skeleton that provides sites for muscle attachment for efficient movement. However, a distinction should be made early that not all chordates are vertebrates. All chordates have the following features at some point in their life (in the case of humans and many other vertebrates; these features may only be present in the embryo):

- **Pharyngeal slits**—A series of openings that connect the inside of the throat to the outside of the "neck." Used to filter water. These are often, but not always, used as gills.

- **Dorsal hollow nerve cord**—A bundle of nerve fibers which runs down the "back." It connects the brain with the lateral muscles and other organs.

- **Notochord**—Cartilaginous rod running underneath and supporting the nerve cord.

- **Post-anal tail**—An extension of the body past the anal opening.

SUBPHYLUM UROCHORDATA (TUNICATES OR SEA SQUIRTS)

Tunicates are sessile animals or planktonic. The structure of the modified adult is very different from the larvae. Larval tunicates show bilateral symmetry, a dorsal nerve chord, a notochord, and a postanal tail. These features are lost when it settles into the adult stage. Adults have a sievelike basket perforated with pharyngeal gill slits and are surrounded by a cellulose sac called a tunic, hence the common name. Water enters through a siphon, is filtered by the basket, and exits though an excurrent siphon. Mucus from the basket collects food which is moved by cilia to the stomach and intestines.

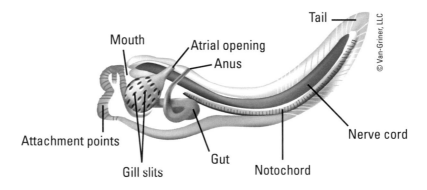

Figure 12.25 Larval Tunicate Structure.

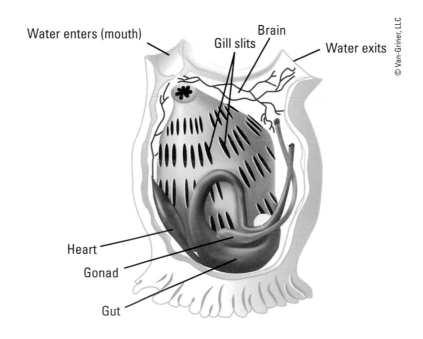

Figure 12.26 Adult Tunicate Structure.

Figure 12.27 Red Sea-Squirts (*Halocynthia papillosa*).

SUBPHYLUM CEPHALOCHORDATA (LANCELETS)

Small, fishlike (but without paired fins or limbs), marine chordates that burrow in sand or mud are referred to as Lancelets or commonly called *Amphioxus.* Like vertebrates, lancelets have a hollow nerve cord running along the back, pharyngeal slits, and a tail that runs past the anus. Unlike vertebrates, the dorsal nerve cord is not protected by bone but by a simpler notochord that extends into the head. This gives the subphylum its name (*cephalo-* meaning "relating to the head"). The nerve cord is only slightly larger in the head region than in the rest of the body, so that lancelets cannot be said to possess a true brain. A poorly developed tail is present but they are not especially good swimmers. While they do possess some cartilage-like material stiffening the gill slits, mouth, and tail, they have no true skeleton. To feed, seawater enters the mouth, passes over the reinforced tissue, and exits through the gills. Food particles caught on tissue eventually make their way to the intestines. Lancelets are studied to gain insight into the evolutionary origins of the vertebrates.

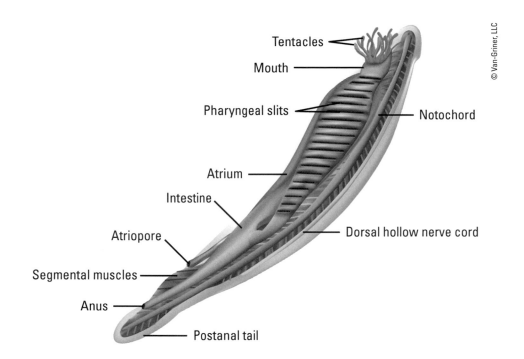

Figure 12.28 Anatomy of the Fish-like Invertebrate, Lancelet.

SUBPHYLUM VERTEBRATA (FISH, BIRDS, AMPHIBIANS, REPTILES, AND MAMMALS)

In this diverse group of animals the notochord in adults is replaced by a vertebral column. This column surrounds and protects the dorsal nerve cord. A distinct head also is seen in every class. In lab today, three classes of vertebrates discussed are fishes and four are terrestrial tetrapods.

CLASS AGNATHA (LAMPREYS AND HAGFISHES)

Lampreys are jawless aquatic vertebrates that have a cartilaginous endoskeleton and notochord. The best-known examples are parasites that use their toothed oral suckers to attach to fish and suck their blood. Although lampreys are sometimes referred to as fish, they are actually quite different from fish and all other vertebrates. Lamprey larvae are called *ammocoetes.* The larvae look very different from the adults, and originally were described as different species. While adult lampreys may range in size from 10 to 100 cm long, the ammocoetes is only one to two centimeters long. The larvae are anatomically quite simple; eventually they undergo a metamorphosis, reorganizing their bodies and developing into the more-complex adult forms. The ammocoetes larva bear a strong resemblance to those of *Branchiostoma* (Subphylum Cephalochordata) and it would be easy to confuse one with the other. Keep in mind, that the lancelet is very small. The larva of the lamprey is similar to the adult cephalochordate.

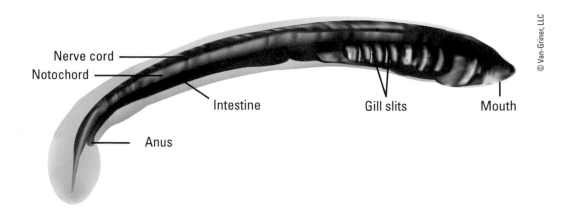

Figure 12.29 Ammocoetes Larva of a Lamprey.

Figure 12.30 Sucking Mouth and Teeth Used to Feed on Fish. Pacific lamprey (*Lampetra tridentata*), a fish characterized by a jawless sucking mouth.

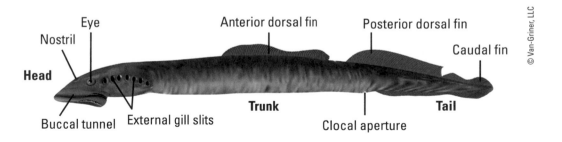

Figure 12.31 Adult Lamprey Anatomy.

CLASS CHONDRICHTHYES (SHARKS, SKATES, AND RAYS)

Oceans are home to fierce predators and scavengers. Sharks and their relatives are at the top of the food chain resulting from many adaptations. Like lampreys, the endoskeleton is tough and composed of cartilage. Unlike lampreys, strong jaws have evolved from modification of anterior gill arches. Other advancements include paired pelvic fins and pectoral fins for stabilization. These features combined with a streamlined body allow for greater maneuvering and speed. The nostrils and skin contain receptors sensitive to smell and detection of electrical currents given off by prey. A lateral line runs along each side of the body and contains sensory cells to detect light vibrations too.

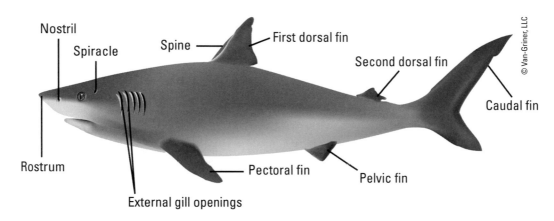

© Van-Griner, LLC

Figure 12.32 External Shark Anatomy.

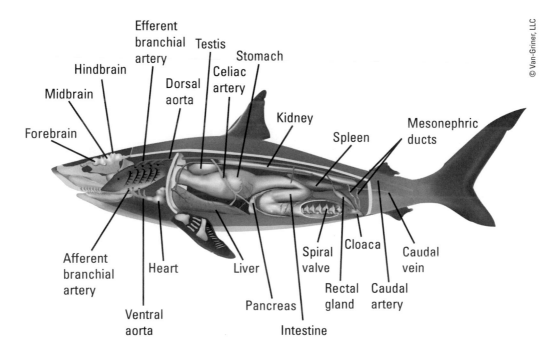

© Van-Griner, LLC

Figure 12.33 Internal Shark Anatomy.

CLASS OSTEICHTHYES (BONY FISH)

Bony fish with over 20,000 identified species represent the most diverse class of vertebrates. Advanced features to emerge include a bony endoskeleton, modified gill arches, and internal air bladders for controlling balance and buoyancy. A movable gill cover, called an operculum, protects the gills. Along each side and branching over the head is a lateral-line system consisting of sensory pits in the skin. Changes in water currents and predators or prey moving near the fish can be detected by the pits.

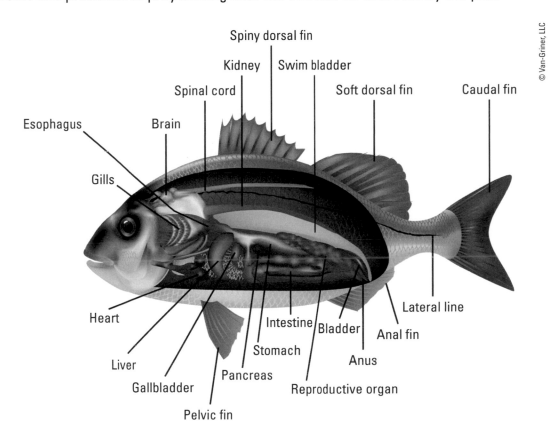

© Van-Griner, LLC

Figure 12.34 Bony Fish Anatomy.

CLASS AMPHIBIA (FROGS, TOADS, AND SALAMANDERS)

The first vertebrates to make the move to land were the amphibians. Earliest amphibians descended from fish with stout and fleshy fins. Amphibians are still tied to water through their life cycle. Adults are terrestrial but lay eggs in water. The eggs are fertilized and hatch into an aquatic larval stage called a tadpole. Tadpoles undergo metamorphosis of body shape as they become adults. Transitioning to land was a significant evolutionary stride made possible by the development of legs, lungs, and a moist vascularized skin to assist in diffusion of oxygen.

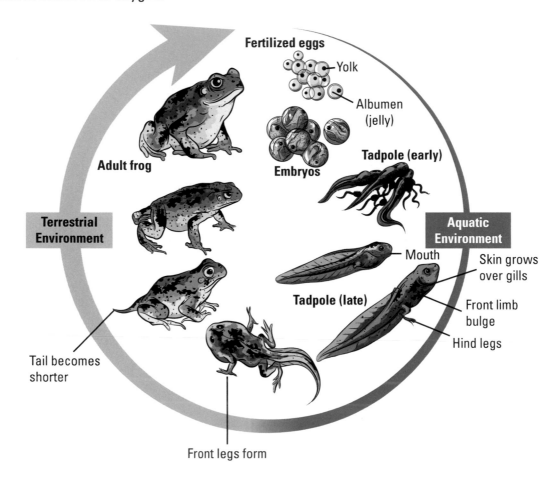

Figure 12.35 Life Cycle of a Common Frog.

CLASS REPTILIA (TURTLES, SNAKES, AND LIZARDS)

True independence from aquatic environments was achieved by reptiles. Reptiles had developed structures to facilitate internal fertilization. This was significant because it led to the amniotic egg, a watertight egg that contained all the essential food sources to support growth and development of an embryo. Unlike amphibians that have a moist skin aiding in respiration, reptiles are covered in dry, scaly skin. The hard skin prevents dehydration and may offer protection against predators. Reptiles have a four-chambered heart and well-developed lungs. Like fish and amphibians, the reptiles are poikilothermic (ectothermic or commonly referred to as cold-blooded) requiring the environment to warm or cool their body.

Figure 12.36 Alligator Hatching.

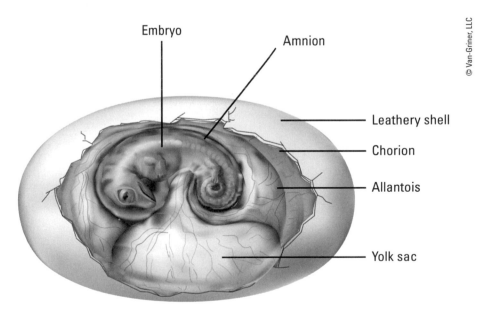

Figure 12.37 Amniotic Egg of Reptile.

CLASS AVES (BIRDS)

The only animals to have feathers are birds. Only a few groups besides birds have the ability to fly. Wings of birds are highly modified forelimbs. Birds are also characterized by the presence of beaks lacking teeth, laying hard-shelled eggs, a high metabolic rate, four-chambered heart, and lightweight but strong skeleton. The eyes of birds are very prominent and vision is a highly developed sense. Unlike previous classes, birds are considered homeothermic (endothermic or commonly called warm-blooded) meaning they maintain a constant body temperature. The musculature of bird breasts is heavy and needed to power the movement of wings. Current research suggests that the lineage of birds traces back to ancestral dinosaurs.

CLASS MAMMALIA

Unlike birds covered by feathers the next class is covered by hair. Mammals are characterized by having an insulating body fat layer and hair to help maintain a constant body temperature as birds do. Mammals tend to have four legs, are active and require a well-developed circulatory system with a four-chambered heart. The efficient circulatory system distributes oxygen, nutrients, and heat. Another unique characteristic of mammals is their ability to give birth to live young and nourish them with milk produced by a female's mammary glands.

Figure 12.38 Female Pig Providing Milk to Her Offspring.

Figure 12.39 Manatee Mother (*Trichechus manatus*) Nursing Calf.

OBSERVE PRESERVED CHORDATE SPECIMENS

1. Obtain one preserved example from each sybphylum and class as specified by your instructor.

2. If available, compare the skeletons of various vertebrate animals.

3. How are the forelimbs of amphibians, reptiles, and birds different from one another?

4. Time permitting, obtain an owl pellet and perform a dissection of its contents.

Table 12.2 Phyla Echninodermata and Chordata.

Phylum	Typical Examples	Key Characteristics	Approximate Number of Named Species
Echinodermata	Sea stars Sea urchins Sand dollars Sea cucumbers		
Chordata	Mammals Fish Reptiles Birds Amphibians		

NOTES

Biology 101 Laboratory Manual

LABORATORY 12 REVIEW
ANIMAL DIVERSITY, PART 2

QUESTIONS

1. How is *Nereis* perfectly adapted for its environment?

   _____

   _____

   _____

   _____

2. What are the fleshy appendages appearing on each segment of *Nereis,* the clam worm? What is their purpose?

   _____

   _____

   _____

   _____

3. What are the three classes of Annelids?

    _____

    _____

    _____

    _____

4. What is a clitellum? What is its purpose? On what animal would you find one?

    _____

    _____

    _____

    _____

5. What was unusual about the segments of scorpions?

    _____

    _____

    _____

    _____

6. What are the three distinct body regions of insects?

    _____

    _____

    _____

    _____

NAME: _____ DATE: _____

7. Why are spiders not considered insects?

_____

_____

_____

_____

8. What is the exoskeleton of arthropods made of?

_____

_____

_____

_____

9. What is the function of the water vascular system of a sea star? What is the madreporite?

_____

_____

_____

_____

10. What is Aristotle's Lantern? What organisms have it?

_____

_____

_____

_____

11. Do sea urchins have arms?

_____

_____

_____

_____

12. What is the pattern that looks like petals of a flower seen on bleached tests of sand dollars?

_____

_____

_____

_____

13. Which phylum is most closely related to our own phylum (Chordata)?

_____

_____

_____

_____

14. What features are unique to the Phylum Chordata?

_____

_____

_____

_____

15. What is meant by homeothermic? Give an example of an animal that is homeothermic.

_____

_____

_____

_____

NOTES